Step by Step Study Guide for GED

MW00635796

300 Steps to Learn All Topics of GED Math Test. Ultimate Tutor to ace GED Math + Two Full Length Practice Tests.

Dr. Abolfazl Nazari

Welcome to GED Math Made Easy 2024

GED step by step, was written to help you pass the GED Math test. The approach that we used in this book is to provide step by step guides to help you understand how mathematical concepts are applied in the GED Math test. Each topic is explained in a simple and easy to understand way. We also included a lot of examples and exercises to help you practice and master the math concepts. Every topic contains the steps you need to follow to solve the problems. Similarly, every example is solved using the steps provided. We are excited to show you what is inside this book. Let's get started!

The content of the book is organized into chapters and then topics. Each topic is explained in a simple and easy to understand way. First thing you will notice is that we have presented the concepts in step by step guides to help you understand how mathematical concepts are applied in the GED Math test.

This is a revolutionary approach to learning math. We believe you will find it very helpful. Every example, similarly, is solved using the steps provided. We also included a lot of examples and exercises to help you practice and master the math concepts.

Our GED Math series include study guides, workbooks, and practice tests. To succeed in the GED Math test, you need to pick the right study materials. We provide you with everything you need to succeed in the GED Math test. We encourage you to explore our GED Math series and use our resources to help you succeed in the GED Math test.

What is included in this book

- ☑ Online resources for additional practice and support.
- ☑ A guide on how to use this book affectively.
- ☑ All GED Math concepts and topics you will be tested on.
- ☑ End of chapter exercises to help you develop the basic math skills.
- ☑ GED Math test tips and strategies.
- ☑ 2 realistic and full-length practice tests with detailed answers.

Effortless Math's GED Online Center

Effortless Math Online GED Center offers a complete study program, including the following:

- ☑ *Step-by-step instructions on how to prepare for the GED Math test*
- ☑ *Numerous GED Math worksheets to help you measure your math skills*
- ☑ *Complete list of GED Math formulas*
- ☑ *Video lessons for all GED Math topics*
- ☑ *Full-length GED Math practice tests*

Visit EffortlessMath.com/GED to find your online GED Math resources.

Scan this QR code

(No Registration Required)

How to Use This Book

This book is designed to simplify the journey of mastering GED Math through a step-by-step approach. Each concept is broken down into manageable steps, followed by examples that are solved using a similar method. Here's how you can make the most out of this book:

- Each topic is explained in a **step-by-step** manner. Begin by understanding the concept and then move on to the examples.
- The examples are solved in a step-by-step fashion, mirroring the approach taken in explaining the concepts. Try to solve these examples on your own before looking at the solution.
- Practice problems are provided at the end of each topic. Use these to test your understanding and reinforce the concepts you've learned.

Maximize Your Learning

1. **Study the Steps:** Pay close attention to the steps outlined in both the concept explanation and the example solutions. This will help you understand the methodology behind solving similar problems.
2. **Work Through Examples:** Actively work through the examples before checking the provided solutions. This active engagement helps in solidifying your understanding of the material.
3. **Practice Regularly:** The practice problems at the end of each section are there to help you apply what you've learned. Regular practice is crucial for mastering the material.

Utilize the Practice Tests

The practice tests are a critical component of your preparation. They offer:

- A chance to apply what you've learned in a test-like environment.
- An opportunity to identify areas where further review is needed.
- Insight into your readiness for the actual GED Math test.

Follow the steps, work through the examples, and use the practice problems and tests to assess and enhance your understanding of GED Math. Good luck!

Contents

1. Fractions and Mixed Numbers

1.1 Simplifying Fractions

Simplifying a fraction means converting it to its lowest terms by ensuring the numerator and denominator no longer share any common factors except 1. When simplified, a fraction represents the same value in its simplest form.

To simplify fractions, follow these steps:

Step 1 Identify a common factor of both the numerator and the denominator, aside from 1. If no such common factor exists, the fraction is already in its simplest form.

Step 2 Divide both the numerator and the denominator by this common factor.

Step 3 Repeat the previous steps until no further common factors can be found, except for 1.

Step 4 Alternatively, find the greatest common divisor (GCD) of both the numerator and the denominator and divide them both by this number for direct simplification.

Example: Simplify $\frac{30}{42}$.

Solution:

Step 1 Identify a common factor. A common factor for 30 and 42, aside from 1, is 2.

Step 2 Divide both the numerator and the denominator by 2: $\frac{30 \div 2}{42 \div 2} = \frac{15}{21}$.

Step 3 Identify a new common factor for 15 and 21, which is 3. Then divide both by 3: $\frac{15 \div 3}{21 \div 3} = \frac{5}{7}$.

step ④   Observe that 5 and 7 do not have any common factors other than 1, so $\frac{5}{7}$ is the simplified fraction. Since the GCD of 30 and 42 is 6, we could also simplify by dividing both the numerator and the denominator directly by 6 to get $\frac{5}{7}$.

1.2   Adding and Subtracting Fractions

Adding and subtracting fractions requires a common denominator. With 'like' fractions (same denominator), combine the numerators. With 'unlike' fractions (different denominators), find equivalent fractions with a common denominator, or use the Least Common Denominator (LCD).

> **Step By Step**   To add or subtract 'like' fractions, follow these steps:
>
> step ① Ensure the fractions have the same denominator.
>
> step ② Add or subtract the numerators while keeping the denominator the same.

> **Step By Step**   To add or subtract 'unlike' fractions, follow these steps:
>
> step ① Find a common denominator for the fractions.
>
> step ② Convert each fraction to an equivalent fraction with the common denominator.
>
> step ③ Add or subtract the new numerators and place the result over the common denominator.
>
> step ④ Simplify the resulting fraction if possible.

Example: Find the sum of two fractions with different denominators, $\frac{1}{3} + \frac{4}{9}$.

Solution: These fractions have different denominators, so they are 'unlike' fractions. We use two methods to find their sum.

Method 1 - Multiplying Denominators:

step ① Multiply the numerator and denominator of each fraction by the denominator of the other fraction.

$$\frac{1 \times 9}{3 \times 9} + \frac{4 \times 3}{9 \times 3} = \frac{9}{27} + \frac{12}{27}$$

Step 2   Add the resulting fractions which now have like denominators.

$$\frac{9}{27} + \frac{12}{27} = \frac{9+12}{27} = \frac{21}{27}$$

Step 3   Simplify the resulting fraction by dividing the numerator and the denominator by their greatest common divisor (GCD).

$$\frac{21}{27} \text{ can be simplified to } \frac{7}{9} \text{ since } \gcd(21,27) = 3.$$

Method 2 - Using LCD:

Step 1   Determine the LCD of the denominators, which is 9.

Step 2   Convert each fraction to have the LCD as its new denominator.

$$\frac{1}{3} = \frac{1 \times 3}{3 \times 3} = \frac{3}{9}, \quad \frac{4}{9} = \frac{4}{9}$$

Step 3   Add the new fractions together.

$$\frac{3}{9} + \frac{4}{9} = \frac{3+4}{9} = \frac{7}{9}$$

1.3   Multiplying and Dividing Fractions

Multiplying and dividing fractions are key skills in understanding how parts of a whole interact with each other. We will investigate the methods for both operations, which are simple once you know the rules.

Step By Step

To multiply fractions, apply these steps:

Step 1   Multiply the numerators (the top numbers) of the fractions to get the new numerator.

Step 2   Multiply the denominators (the bottom numbers) of the fractions to get the new denominator.

Step 3   Simplify the resulting fraction to the lowest terms.

Step By Step

To divide fractions, apply these steps:

Step 1 Keep the first fraction as it is (the dividend).

Step 2 Change the division sign to a multiplication sign.

Step 3 Flip the second fraction (the divisor), taking the reciprocal.

Step 4 Multiply the numerators of the two fractions to get the new numerator.

Step 5 Multiply the denominators of the two fractions to get the new denominator.

Step 6 Simplify the resulting fraction to the lowest terms.

Example: Multiply $\frac{3}{6} \times \frac{6}{7}$.

Solution:

Step 1 Multiply the numerators together: $3 \times 6 = 18$.

Step 2 Multiply the denominators together: $6 \times 7 = 42$.

Step 3 Write the multiplication result as a fraction and simplify: $\frac{18}{42} = \frac{3}{7}$ after dividing both the numerator and the denominator by 6.

Example: Divide $\frac{4}{5} \div \frac{3}{7}$.

Solution:

Step 1 Keep the first fraction: $\frac{4}{5}$.

Step 2 Change the division sign to multiplication and flip the second fraction: $\frac{4}{5} \times \frac{7}{3}$.

Step 3 Multiply the numerators: $4 \times 7 = 28$.

Step 4 Multiply the denominators: $5 \times 3 = 15$.

Step 5 Combine the results and state the final simplified fraction: $\frac{28}{15}$.

1.4   Adding Mixed Numbers

Adding mixed numbers involves combining the whole numbers and the fractional parts separately and then converting any improper fractions into mixed numbers if necessary.

Step By Step

To add mixed numbers, apply these steps:

Step 1   Split each mixed number into its whole number and fractional parts.

Step 2   Add the whole numbers together.

Step 3   Add the fractional parts together.

Step 4   If the sum of the fractions is an improper fraction, convert it to a mixed number.

Step 5   Combine the sum of whole numbers with the sum of the fractions, now properly expressed as a mixed number or proper fraction.

Example: Add the following mixed numbers $2\frac{3}{4} + 3\frac{5}{8}$.

Solution:

Step 1   Split into whole numbers and fractions: 2 and $\frac{3}{4}$, 3 and $\frac{5}{8}$.

Step 2   Add the whole numbers: $2 + 3 = 5$.

Step 3   Add the fractions: $\frac{3}{4} + \frac{5}{8} = \frac{6}{8} + \frac{5}{8} = \frac{11}{8}$.

Step 4   Change the improper fraction to a mixed number: $\frac{11}{8} = 1\frac{3}{8}$.

Step 5   Combine the whole numbers and fractions: $5 + 1\frac{3}{8} = 6\frac{3}{8}$.

So, $2\frac{3}{4} + 3\frac{5}{8} = 6\frac{3}{8}$.

Example: Add the following mixed numbers $1\frac{2}{3} + 2\frac{3}{4}$.

Solution:

Step 1   Split into whole numbers and fractions: 1 and $\frac{2}{3}$, 2 and $\frac{3}{4}$.

Step 2   Add the whole numbers: $1 + 2 = 3$.

Step 3   Add the fractions: $\frac{2}{3} + \frac{3}{4} = \frac{8}{12} + \frac{9}{12} = \frac{17}{12}$.

Step 4   Change the improper fraction to a mixed number: $\frac{17}{12} = 1\frac{5}{12}$.

Step 5   Combine the whole numbers and fractions: $3 + 1\frac{5}{12} = 4\frac{5}{12}$.

So, $1\frac{2}{3} + 2\frac{3}{4} = 4\frac{5}{12}$.

1.5   Subtracting Mixed Numbers

Subtraction of mixed numbers involves conversion to improper fractions, finding a common denominator, subtracting the fractions, and simplifying the result.

To subtract mixed numbers, apply these steps:

Step 1   Convert the mixed numbers into improper fractions.

Step 2   Find equivalent fractions with a common denominator if they have different denominators.

Step 3   Subtract the second fraction from the first.

Step 4   Simplify the result to the lowest terms possible.

Step 5   If the result is an improper fraction, convert it back into a mixed number.

Example: Subtract $2\frac{1}{5} - 1\frac{1}{4}$.

   Solution:

Step 1   Convert to improper fractions: $2\frac{1}{5} = \frac{2\times5+1}{5} = \frac{11}{5}$, $1\frac{1}{4} = \frac{1\times4+1}{4} = \frac{5}{4}$.

Step 2   Find a common denominator and subtract:

$$\frac{11}{5} - \frac{5}{4} = \frac{44-25}{20} = \frac{19}{20}.$$

1.6   Multiplying and Dividing Mixed Numbers

Multiplying and dividing mixed numbers requires converting them into improper fractions, carrying out the arithmetic operation, and if necessary, converting the result back into a mixed number.

To multiply mixed numbers, apply these steps:

Step 1   Convert each mixed number to an improper fraction.

Step 2   Multiply the numerators of the fractions to find the new numerator.

Step 3   Multiply the denominators of the fractions to find the new denominator.

Step 4   If needed, simplify the resulting fraction.

Step 5   Convert the result back to a mixed number if the fraction is improper.

Step By Step

To divide mixed numbers, apply these steps:

Step 1   Convert each mixed number to an improper fraction.

Step 2   Apply the "Keep, Change, Flip" rule: keep the first fraction, change division to multiplication, and flip (take the reciprocal of) the second fraction.

Step 3   Multiply the numerators to find the new numerator.

Step 4   Multiply the denominators to find the new denominator.

Step 5   Simplify the resulting fraction if needed.

Step 6   Convert the simplified fraction back to a mixed number if it is improper.

Example: Multiply $4\frac{2}{5} \times 2\frac{3}{4}$.

Solution:

Step 1   Convert the mixed numbers into improper fractions. $4\frac{2}{5} = \frac{4\times5+2}{5} = \frac{22}{5}$ and $2\frac{3}{4} = \frac{2\times4+3}{4} = \frac{11}{4}$.

Step 2   Multiply the numerators together to get the new numerator. Multiply the denominators together to get the new denominator. Thus, you perform $\frac{22}{5} \times \frac{11}{4} = \frac{22\times11}{5\times4} = \frac{242}{20}$.

Step 3   Simplify the resulting fraction to $\frac{121}{10}$.

Step 4   Convert the improper fraction into a mixed number: $\frac{121}{10} = 12\frac{1}{10}$.

Example: Divide $3\frac{1}{4} \div 2\frac{2}{3}$.

Solution:

Step 1   Convert the given mixed numbers into improper fractions. $3\frac{1}{4} = \frac{3\times4+1}{4} = \frac{13}{4}$ and $2\frac{2}{3} = \frac{2\times3+2}{3} = \frac{8}{3}$.

Step 2   Use the "Keep, Change, Flip" rule to change the division into multiplication and to flip the second fraction: $\frac{13}{4} \div \frac{8}{3} = \frac{13}{4} \times \frac{3}{8} = \frac{13\times3}{4\times8} = \frac{39}{32}$.

Step 3   The resulting fraction $\frac{39}{32}$ is already simplified.

Step 4   Convert the improper fraction to a mixed number: $1\frac{7}{32}$.

1.7   Practices

Simplify Each Fraction:

1) $\frac{88}{132}$.

2) $\frac{35}{49}$.

3) $\frac{126}{42}$.

4) $\frac{8}{128}$.

5) $\frac{54}{108}$.

Solve:

6) Find the sum of $\frac{1}{2}$ and $\frac{3}{4}$.

7) Subtract $\frac{5}{8}$ from $\frac{7}{8}$.

8) What is the difference between $\frac{2}{5}$ and $\frac{3}{10}$?

9) Add $\frac{3}{7}$ and $\frac{4}{7}$.

10) Calculate the sum of $\frac{2}{5}$, $\frac{1}{2}$ and $\frac{3}{4}$.

Solve:

11) Multiply $\frac{4}{7} \times \frac{5}{8}$.

12) Divide $\frac{7}{10} \div \frac{3}{5}$.

13) Simplify $\frac{4 \times 6}{3 \times 4}$.

14) Divide $2\frac{1}{2} \div \frac{1}{4}$.

15) Multiply $\frac{3}{5} \times \frac{15}{9}$.

Fill in the Blank:

16) $3\frac{1}{2} + 2\frac{2}{3} =$ _____.

17) $4\frac{1}{2} +$ _____ $= 9\frac{1}{2}$.

18) $3\frac{1}{3} + 2\frac{\quad}{3} = 6$.

19) $2\frac{1}{2} +$ _____ $= 3\frac{5}{6}$.

Select One:

20) What will be the improper fraction form of the mixed number $2\frac{1}{3}$.

A) $\frac{1}{2}$

B) $\frac{6}{2}$

C) $\frac{7}{3}$

D) $\frac{5}{3}$

21) Let us assume we have the fractions $\frac{7}{4}$ and $\frac{3}{2}$. What would be the equivalent fractions with the same denominator?

A) $\frac{14}{8}$ and $\frac{16}{8}$

B) $\frac{21}{8}$ and $\frac{12}{8}$

C) $\frac{7}{8}$ and $\frac{9}{8}$

D) $\frac{14}{8}$ and $\frac{12}{8}$

22) $2\frac{1}{2} - 1\frac{3}{4}$ equals:

A) $1\frac{3}{4}$

B) $1\frac{1}{4}$

C) $\frac{3}{4}$

D) $\frac{1}{4}$

23) By subtracting two mixed numbers, we always get a(n):

A) Decimal

B) Fraction

C) Mixed Number

D) It depends on the numbers

24) $3\frac{3}{4} - 2\frac{2}{3}$ equals:

A) $1\frac{1}{12}$

B) $1\frac{11}{12}$

C) $\frac{5}{12}$

D) $1\frac{5}{12}$

Simplify Each Expression:

25) $7\frac{1}{3} \times 2\frac{2}{5} =$

26) $4\frac{1}{5} \times 5\frac{1}{2} =$

27) $3\frac{3}{4} \times 1\frac{1}{3} =$

28) $3\frac{1}{2} \times 1\frac{1}{4} =$

29) $2\frac{1}{3} \times 3\frac{1}{2} =$

Solve:

30) $3\frac{1}{2} \div 2\frac{2}{3} =$

31) $5\frac{1}{4} \div 3\frac{2}{5} =$

32) $4\frac{2}{3} \div 1\frac{2}{3} =$

33) $6\frac{1}{2} \div 2\frac{1}{4} =$

34) $7\frac{3}{4} \div 4\frac{1}{2} =$

Answer Keys

1) $\frac{2}{3}$

2) $\frac{5}{7}$

3) 3

4) $\frac{1}{16}$

5) $\frac{1}{2}$

6) $\frac{5}{4}$

7) $\frac{1}{4}$

8) $\frac{1}{10}$

9) 1

10) $\frac{33}{20}$

11) $\frac{5}{14}$

12) $\frac{7}{6}$

13) 2

14) 10

15) 1

16) $6\frac{1}{6}$

17) 5

18) 2

19) $1\frac{1}{3}$

20) C) $\frac{7}{3}$

21) D) $\frac{14}{8}$ and $\frac{12}{8}$

22) C) $\frac{3}{4}$

23) D) It depends on the numbers.

24) A) $1\frac{1}{12}$

25) $17\frac{3}{5}$

26) $23\frac{1}{10}$

27) 5

28) $4\frac{3}{8}$

29) $8\frac{1}{6}$

30) $1\frac{5}{16}$

31) $1\frac{37}{68}$

32) $2\frac{4}{5}$

33) $2\frac{8}{9}$

34) $1\frac{13}{18}$

Answers with Explanation

1) The GCD of 88 and 132 is 44. So, $\frac{88}{132} = \frac{88 \div 44}{132 \div 44} = \frac{2}{3}$.

2) The GCD of 35 and 49 is 7. So, $\frac{35}{49} = \frac{35 \div 7}{49 \div 7} = \frac{5}{7}$.

3) The GCD of 126 and 42 is 42. So, $\frac{126}{42} = \frac{126 \div 42}{42 \div 42} = \frac{3}{1} = 3$.

4) The GCD of 8 and 128 is 8. So, $\frac{8}{128} = \frac{8 \div 8}{128 \div 8} = \frac{1}{16}$.

5) The GCD of 54 and 108 is 54. So, $\frac{54}{108} = \frac{54 \div 54}{108 \div 54} = \frac{1}{2}$.

6) First, convert $\frac{1}{2}$ to have a denominator of 4, which is $\frac{2}{4}$. Then, add it to $\frac{3}{4}$ to get $\frac{2}{4} + \frac{3}{4} = \frac{5}{4}$.

7) Both fractions have the same denominator, so we subtract the numerators directly: $\frac{7}{8} - \frac{5}{8} = \frac{2}{8} = \frac{1}{4}$.

8) The least common denominator for 5 and 10 is 10. We use the formula $\frac{2 \times 2}{5 \times 2} - \frac{3}{10} = \frac{4-3}{10} = \frac{1}{10}$.

9) Both fractions have the same denominator, so we add the numerators directly. $\frac{3}{7} + \frac{4}{7} = \frac{7}{7} = 1$.

10) To sum up the three fractions, we find the least common denominator which is 20 and transform each fraction to get equivalent fractions that all have the denominator of 20. Thus the sum becomes $\frac{8}{20} + \frac{10}{20} + \frac{15}{20} = \frac{33}{20}$.

11) We multiply the numerators: $4 \times 5 = 20$ and the denominators: $7 \times 8 = 56$, giving us $\frac{20}{56}$. Then, we simplify the fraction by dividing the numerator and the denominator by their greatest common divisor, which is 4; obtaining $\frac{5}{14}$.

12) We change the division to multiplication and flip the reciprocal of the second fraction. So, $\frac{7}{10} \div \frac{3}{5}$ becomes $\frac{7}{10} \times \frac{5}{3} = \frac{35}{30}$. We simplify this to $\frac{7}{6}$.

13) First, we perform the multiplications, which gives us $\frac{24}{12}$. Then, we simplify this to 2.

14) We firstly convert the mixed number to an improper fraction: $2\frac{1}{2} = \frac{5}{2}$. Now, we apply the "keep, change, flip" rule, and the division problem $\frac{5}{2} \div \frac{1}{4}$ becomes $\frac{5}{2} \times \frac{4}{1}$, which simplifies to 10.

15) We multiply our numerators giving us 45, and do the same for the denominators giving us 45. Our division problem is $\frac{45}{45}$ which simplifies to 1 because any number divided by itself equals 1.

16) The whole numbers 3 and 2 add up to give 5. The fractions

$$\frac{1}{2} + \frac{2}{3} = \frac{3}{6} + \frac{4}{6} = \frac{7}{6} = 1\frac{1}{6}.$$

Total result is then $5 + 1\frac{1}{6} = 6\frac{1}{6}$.

17) $4\frac{1}{2} + 5 = 9\frac{1}{2}$.

18) $3\frac{1}{3} + 2\frac{2}{3} = 5\frac{3}{3} = 6$.

19) $3\frac{5}{6} - 2\frac{1}{2} = 1\frac{2}{6} = 1\frac{1}{3}$.

20) The mixed number $2\frac{1}{3}$ converts to an improper fraction $\frac{2\times3+1}{3} = \frac{7}{3}$.

21) We find equivalent fractions of $\frac{7}{4}$ and $\frac{3}{2}$ with the same denominator 8, which are $\frac{14}{8}$ and $\frac{12}{8}$ respectively.

22) By following the steps of subtracting mixed numbers, we get $2\frac{1}{2} - 1\frac{3}{4} = \frac{5}{2} - \frac{7}{4} = \frac{3}{4}$.

23) The result of subtracting two mixed numbers could be a whole number, decimal, fraction or mixed number depending on the initial numbers.

24) Following the proper steps for subtracting mixed numbers, we get $3\frac{3}{4} - 2\frac{2}{3} = 3\frac{9}{12} - 2\frac{8}{12} = 1\frac{1}{12}$.

25) Convert to improper fractions.

$$7\frac{1}{3} = \frac{22}{3}, \qquad 2\frac{2}{5} = \frac{12}{5}.$$

Multiply: $\frac{22}{3} \times \frac{12}{5} = \frac{264}{15}$. Convert to mixed number: $\frac{264\div3}{15\div3} = \frac{88}{5} = 17\frac{3}{5}$.

26) Convert to improper fractions: $4\frac{1}{5} = \frac{21}{5}, 5\frac{1}{2} = \frac{11}{2}$.

   Multiply: $\frac{21}{5} \times \frac{11}{2} = \frac{231}{10}$.

   Convert to mixed number: $\frac{231}{10} = 23\frac{1}{10}$.

27) Convert to improper fractions: $3\frac{3}{4} = \frac{15}{4}, 1\frac{1}{3} = \frac{4}{3}$.

   Multiply: $\frac{15}{4} \times \frac{4}{3} = \frac{60}{12}$.

   Simplify to get: $\frac{60}{12} = 5$.

28) Convert to improper fractions: $3\frac{1}{2} = \frac{7}{2}, 1\frac{1}{4} = \frac{5}{4}$.

Multiply: $\frac{7}{2} \times \frac{5}{4} = \frac{35}{8}$.

Convert to mixed number: $\frac{35}{8} = 4\frac{3}{8}$.

29) Convert to improper fractions: $2\frac{1}{3} = \frac{7}{3}, 3\frac{1}{2} = \frac{7}{2}$.

Multiply: $\frac{7}{3} \times \frac{7}{2} = \frac{49}{6}$.

Convert to mixed number: $\frac{49}{6} = 8\frac{1}{6}$.

30) First, convert the mixed numbers to improper fractions: $3\frac{1}{2} = \frac{7}{2}, 2\frac{2}{3} = \frac{8}{3}$. Then apply the "Keep, Change, Flip" rule: $\frac{7}{2} \div \frac{8}{3} = \frac{7}{2} \times \frac{3}{8} = \frac{21}{16}$, which simplifies to $1\frac{5}{16}$ in mixed number form.

31) Convert the mixed numbers to improper fractions: $5\frac{1}{4} = \frac{21}{4}, 3\frac{2}{5} = \frac{17}{5}$. Apply the "Keep, Change, Flip" rule: $\frac{21}{4} \div \frac{17}{5} = \frac{21}{4} \times \frac{5}{17} = \frac{105}{68}$, which simplifies to $1\frac{37}{68}$ in mixed number form.

32) Convert the mixed numbers to improper fractions: $4\frac{2}{3} = \frac{14}{3}, 1\frac{2}{3} = \frac{5}{3}$. Apply the "Keep, Change, Flip" rule: $\frac{14}{3} \div \frac{5}{3} = \frac{14}{3} \times \frac{3}{5} = \frac{42}{15} = \frac{14}{5}$, which simplifies to $2\frac{4}{5}$ in mixed number form.

33) First, convert the mixed numbers to improper fractions: $6\frac{1}{2} = \frac{13}{2}, 2\frac{1}{4} = \frac{9}{4}$. Then apply the "Keep, Change, Flip" rule: $\frac{13}{2} \div \frac{9}{4} = \frac{13}{2} \times \frac{4}{9} = \frac{52}{18} = \frac{26}{9}$, which simplifies to $2\frac{8}{9}$ in mixed number form.

34) Convert the mixed numbers to improper fractions: $7\frac{3}{4} = \frac{31}{4}, 4\frac{1}{2} = \frac{9}{2}$. Apply the "Keep, Change, Flip" rule: $\frac{31}{4} \div \frac{9}{2} = \frac{31}{4} \times \frac{2}{9} = \frac{62}{36} = \frac{31}{18}$, which simplifies to $1\frac{13}{18}$ in mixed number form.

2. Decimals

2.1   Comparing Decimals

Decimals are a way of representing fractions with a decimal point separating the whole number from the fractional part. To compare decimals, it is essential to understand the value of each digit according to its position relative to the decimal point.

Step By Step   To compare decimal numbers, apply these steps:

Step 1   Align the numbers with the decimal points in a column, so all the corresponding place values line up.

Step 2   Starting from the left, compare digits in the same place value.

Step 3   If the digits are the same, move one place value to the right and compare the next set of digits.

Step 4   Continue until you find digits that are different or until you've compared all digits.

Step 5   The number with the greater digit in the first place value that differs is the larger number.

Step 6   If all compared digits are the same, the numbers are equal.

Example: Let us compare two decimal numbers 0.05 and 0.50.

  Solution:

Step 5   Align the decimal points: 0.05 is under 0.50.

Step 6   Compare the first non-zero digit after the decimal point: 0.05 has 0 in the tenths place, while 0.50 has 5 in the tenths place.

Step 7   Since 5 is greater than 0, we conclude that 0.05 is less than 0.50, represented as $0.05 < 0.50$.

Example: Now let us compare 0.0829 and 0.329.

  Solution:

Step 1   Align the decimal points: 0.0829 is under 0.329.

Step 2   Start by comparing the digits in the tenths place: 0.0829 has 0 and 0.329 has 3.

Step 3   Since 3 is greater than 0, we conclude that 0.0829 is less than 0.329, represented as $0.0829 < 0.329$.

2.2   Rounding Decimals

Rounding decimals is an essential process in mathematics to simplify numbers and make them easier to manage when precise accuracy is unnecessary.

Step By Step

    To round decimals, apply these steps:

Step 1   Identify the digit in the place value to which you want to round.

Step 2   Look at the next smallest place value to the right. If this digit is 5 or greater, increase the digit you're rounding to by 1.

Step 3   If the digit to the right is less than 5, keep the digit you are rounding to the same.

Step 4   Eliminate all digits to the right of the place value you're rounding to.

Example: Round 3.4278 to the nearest thousandths.

  Solution:

Step 1   Identify the thousandths place. The digit is 7.

Step 2   Look at the ten-thousandths place to the right. The digit is 8, which is greater than 5, so add 1 to the thousandths place.

Step 3   The number in the thousandths place is incremented to 8.

Step 4   Eliminate all digits to the right of the thousandths place, resulting in 4.428.

Example: Round 2.4126 to the nearest hundredths.

    Solution:

Step 1   Identify the hundredths place. The digit is 1.

Step 2   Look at the thousandths place to the right. The digit is 2, which is less than 5. Keep the hundredths place the same.

Step 3   The digit in the hundredths place remains 1.

Step 4   Remove all digits to the right of the hundredths place, resulting in 2.41.

2.3   Adding and Subtracting Decimals

Adding and subtracting decimals is a fundamental concept in mathematics, involving the alignment and manipulation of numbers to perform arithmetic operations.

Step By Step

    To add or subtract decimals, apply these steps:

Step 1   Line up the Decimal Points: Write the numbers in column format with decimal points aligned vertically to match digits of the same place value.

Step 2   Add Zeros to Equalize the Number of Digits: Append zeros to the end of any decimal number that has fewer digits than the others to make the number of digits equal.

Step 3   Use Column Addition or Subtraction: Perform the addition or subtraction by starting from the rightmost digit and moving left, handling each column separately.

Example: Add $2.6 + 5.13$.

    Solution:

Step 1   Line up the decimal numbers by writing them vertically, one under the other:

$$
\begin{array}{r}
2.6 \\
+5.13 \\
\end{array}
$$

Step 2   Add a zero to the first number to equalize the number of decimal digits:

$$2.60$$
$$+5.13$$

Step 3   Perform column addition starting with the hundredths place: $0 + 3 = 3$, then the tenths place: $6 + 1 = 7$, and the ones place: $2 + 5 = 7$ to find $2.6 + 5.13 = 7.73$.

Example: Find: $6.47 - 5.33$.

  Solution:

Step 1   Begin by lining up the decimal numbers vertically:

$$6.47$$
$$-5.33$$

Step 2   Subtract starting from the hundredths place: $7 - 3 = 4$, then from the tenths place: $4 - 3 = 1$, and finally the ones place: $6 - 5 = 1$ to get $6.47 - 5.33 = 1.14$.

2.4   Multiplying and Dividing Decimals

When dealing with decimals, understanding how to multiply and divide them is crucial for mathematical proficiency. Here is how you can do it.

Step
By
Step
    To multiply decimals, apply these steps:

Step 1   Ignore the decimal point and multiply the numbers as if they were integers.

Step 2   Count the total number of decimal places in both of the original numbers.

Step 3   Place the decimal point in the product so that the number of decimal places matches the count from the previous step.

Step By Step
    Follow these steps to divide decimals:

Step 1   If the divisor is a decimal, move the decimal point to the right to make it a whole number, and do the same with the dividend.

Step 2   Proceed with the division using the adjusted numbers, applying the standard division process.

Example: Let us find the product of 0.57×0.32.

   Solution:

Step 1   Multiply the numbers without considering the decimal point: $57 \times 32 = 1824$.

Step 2   Count the decimal places in the original factors: 0.57 has 2 and 0.32 also has 2, which gives a total of 4 decimal places.

Step 3   Place the decimal point in 1824 to create 4 decimal places: 0.1824.

Example: Calculate the quotient $3.62 \div 0.8$.

   Solution:

Step 1   Convert the divisor into a whole number by moving the decimal one place to the right to get 8, and do the same to the dividend to get 36.2.

Step 2   Proceed with the division using the adjusted numbers: $36.2 \div 8 = 4.525$.

2.5   Practices

Select One:

1) Which option correctly compares the decimals 0.75 and 0.8?

   A) $0.75 > 0.8$

   B) $0.75 < 0.8$

   C) $0.75 = 0.8$

2) Choose the correct comparison for 0.213 and 0.2131?

   A) $0.213 > 0.2131$

   B) $0.213 < 0.2131$

   C) $0.213 = 0.2131$

3) Select the correct comparison for the decimals 0.097 and 0.0970?

    A) $0.097 > 0.0970$

    B) $0.097 < 0.0970$

    C) $0.097 = 0.0970$

4) Choose the correct comparison for the decimals 0.301 and 0.0301?

    A) $0.301 > 0.0301$

    B) $0.301 < 0.0301$

    C) $0.301 = 0.0301$

5) What is the correct comparison for the decimals 0.649 and 0.6490?

    A) $0.649 > 0.6490$

    B) $0.649 < 0.6490$

    C) $0.649 = 0.6490$

Fill in the Blank:

6) Round 10.4785 to nearest tenths. The answer is _____.

7) Round 11.342 to nearest ones. The answer is _____.

8) Round 28.6532 to nearest hundredths. The answer is _____.

Solve:

9) $5.8 + 7.69 =$

10) $8.87 - 0.98 =$

11) $1.002 + 2.3 =$

12) $15.8 - 7.75 =$

13) $9.76 + 2.89 =$

Fill in the Blank:

14) $0.25 \times 0.8 =$ _____.

15) $0.64 \div 0.8 = $ _____.

16) $0.6 \times 0.3 = $ _____.

17) $3.2 \div 0.8 = $ _____.

18) $0.75 \times 0.4 = $ _____.

Answer Keys

1) B) $0.75 < 0.8$

2) B) $0.213 < 0.2131$

3) C) $0.097 = 0.0970$

4) A) $0.301 > 0.0301$

5) C) $0.649 = 0.6490$

6) 10.5

7) 11

8) 28.65

9) 13.49

10) 7.89

11) 3.302

12) 8.05

13) 12.65

14) 0.2

15) 0.8

16) 0.18

17) 4

18) 0.3

Answers with Explanation

1) Since the digit at the tenths place in 0.8 is 8 and the digit at the same place in 0.75 is 7, we can conclude that 0.75 is less than 0.8.

2) 0.213 is less than 0.2131 because 0.2131 has an additional digit in the ten-thousandths place.

3) The decimals 0.097 and 0.0970 are equal. The zero at the end of 0.0970 does not change its value.

4) 0.301 is greater than 0.0301 because 0.301 has the digit 3 at the tenths place, while 0.0301 has the digit 3 at the hundredths place.

5) The decimals 0.649 and 0.6490 are equal. The zero at the end of 0.6490 does not change its value.

6) The digit in the hundredths place is 7, which is greater than 5. So, we add 1 to the digit in the tenths place.

7) The digit in the tenths place is 3, which is less than 5. So, we round down and keep the digit in the ones place the same.

8) The digit in the thousandths place is 3, which is less than 5. So, we keep the digit in the hundredths place the same.

9) Align and add the decimals.

$$\begin{array}{r} 5.80 \\ +7.69 \\ \hline 13.49 \end{array}$$

10) Align the decimals of 8.87 and 0.98. Subtract each column starting from the right:

$$\begin{array}{r} 8.87 \\ -0.98 \\ \hline 7.89 \end{array}$$

In the hundredths place: $7 - 8$ (borrow from tenths), resulting in 9. In the tenths place: $8 - 9$ (borrow from ones), resulting in 8. In the ones place: $7 - 0 = 7$. So, $8.87 - 0.98 = 7.89$.

11) Align and add the decimals.

$$
\begin{array}{r}
1.002 \\
+2.300 \\
\hline
3.302
\end{array}
$$

12) Align and subtract the decimals.

$$
\begin{array}{r}
15.80 \\
-7.75 \\
\hline
8.05
\end{array}
$$

13) Align and add the decimals.

$$
\begin{array}{r}
9.76 \\
+2.89 \\
\hline
12.65
\end{array}
$$

14) The result of $25 \times 8 = 200$. Counting the number of places after the decimal in the original numbers, we have $2 + 1 = 3$. Hence, setting the decimal point three places from the right in 200, our answer is 0.200 or 0.2.

15) After converting 0.8 to a whole number, 8, we also convert the dividend, resulting in 6.4. Then, $6.4 \div 8 = 0.8$.

16) The result of $6 \times 3 = 18$. There are $1 + 1 = 2$ decimal places in the original numbers, so we place the decimal two places from the right to get 0.18.

17) By translating the divisor and dividend into whole numbers, we get $32 \div 8 = 4$.

18) The result of $75 \times 4 = 300$. Counting the decimal places $2 + 1 = 3$ in the original numbers, and placing the decimal accordingly, we get 0.3.

3. Integers and Order of Operations

3.1   Adding and Subtracting Integers

Integers can be positive, negative, or zero. Understanding how to add and subtract integers is fundamental in mathematics.

Step By Step

To add integers, apply these steps:

Step 1   Determine if the integers have the same or different signs.

Step 2   For same signs, add their absolute values and keep the sign.

Step 3   For different signs, subtract the smaller absolute value from the larger one and take the sign of the integer with the larger absolute value.

Example: Calculate $(-4) + (+15)$.

Solution:

Step 1   Determine the signs of the integers (-4 is negative, $+15$ is positive) which are different.

Step 2   Compare the absolute values where 15 is larger than 4.

Step 3   Subtract the smaller from the larger one ($15 - 4 = 11$) and take the sign of the larger absolute value (positive). Hence, $(-4) + (+15) = 11$.

Step By Step

To subtract integers, follow these steps:

Step 1   Identify the two numbers involved in the subtraction.

Step 2   Determine the opposite of the integer being subtracted.

Step 3   Add the opposite to the original number.

Example: Calculate $-3 - (-9)$.

   Solution:

Step 1   Identify the integers -3 and -9.

Step 2   Determine the opposite of -9, which is $+9$.

Step 3   Add the opposite to the first integer: $-3 + 9 = 6$. Thus, $-3 - (-9) = 6$.

3.2   Multiplying and Dividing Integers

Multiplying and dividing integers involve simple rules regarding the signs of the numbers involved. Understanding these rules is essential to carry out arithmetic operations correctly.

Step By Step

To multiply or divide integers, apply these steps:

Step 1   Determine the sign of each integer.

Step 2   Apply the sign rule based on the combination of signs:

- Negative $\times$ Negative = Positive
- Negative $\times$ Positive = Negative
- Positive $\times$ Positive = Positive
- Positive $\times$ Negative = Negative

Step 3   Carry out the multiplication or division ignoring the signs.

Step 4   Attach the determined sign to the result from the previous step.

Example: Calculate $5 \times (-7)$.

   Solution:

Step 1   Identifying the signs: 5 is positive, and -7 is negative.

Step 2   Apply the sign rule: Positive × Negative = Negative.

Step 3   Multiply the absolute values: $5 \times 7 = 35$.

Step 4   Attach the sign to the result: The product is -35.

Example: Calculate $(-32) \div (-4)$.

  Solution:

Step 1   Identifying the signs: Both -32 and -4 are negative.

Step 2   Apply the sign rule: Negative $\div$ Negative = Positive.

Step 3   Divide the absolute values: $32 \div 4 = 8$.

Step 4   Attach the positive sign to the result: The quotient is 8.

3.3   Order of Operations

In mathematics, the order of operations is the sequence that defines the correct order to perform arithmetic operations. This is essential to solve expressions accurately.

Step By Step
To correctly perform the order of operations, apply these steps:

Step 1   First, calculate expressions inside parentheses (also includes brackets and braces).

Step 2   Second, evaluate exponents (or powers).

Step 3   Third, perform multiplication and division from left to right.

Step 4   Finally, perform addition and subtraction from left to right.

Example: Calculate $(3+6) \div (3^2 \div 9)$.

  Solution:

Step 1   Perform calculations inside parentheses: $3+6 = 9$ and $3^2 \div 9 = 9 \div 9 = 1$.

Step 2   Following this, perform the division operation: $9 \div 1 = 9$. Therefore, the solution is $(3+6) \div (3^2 \div 9) = 9$.

Example: Calculate $-5 \times \left[(3 \times 4) \div (2 \times 6) \right]$.

  Solution:

Step 1   Calculate within brackets:

$$-5 \times \left[(12) \div (12) \right] = -5 \times 1.$$

$Step2$ Then, perform the multiplication: $-5 \times 1 = -5$. The result is $-5 \times \left[(3 \times 4) \div (2 \times 6) \right] = -5$.

3.4   Absolute Value

The absolute value of a number is its distance from zero on the number line, ignoring its sign. It is denoted by $|x|$ for a number x, and it is defined as x if x is non-negative and $-x$ if x is negative.

Step By Step   To find the absolute value of a number, apply these steps:

$Step1$ Identify the number of which you want to find the absolute value.

$Step2$ If the number is non-negative (greater than or equal to zero), then the absolute value is the number itself.

$Step3$ If the number is negative (less than zero), then the absolute value is the opposite of the number, which is its positive counterpart.

Example: Calculate $|17 - 4| \times 3$.

   Solution:

$Step1$ Apply the absolute value operation: $|17 - 4| = |13|$.

$Step2$ Since 13 is non-negative, the absolute value is the number itself: $|13| = 13$.

$Step3$ Multiply by 3 to get the final result: $13 \times 3 = 39$.

Example: Calculate $\frac{|-15|}{3} \times |4 - 8|$.

   Solution:

$Step1$ Find the absolute value of -15: $|-15| = 15$.

$Step2$ Divide by 3: $\frac{15}{3} = 5$.

$Step3$ Find the absolute value of $4 - 8$: $|4 - 8| = |-4| = 4$.

$Step4$ Multiply the results to get the final answer: $5 \times 4 = 20$.

3.5   Practices

    Calculate:

1) Calculate $-5 - 3$.

2) Calculate $-4 + 5$.

3) Calculate $6 + 3 - (-4)$.

4) Calculate $-1 - 4 - (-5)$.

5) Calculate $10 - 3 - 2$.

Calculate:

6) Calculate $4 \div (-2)$.

7) Calculate $(-6) \times (5)$.

8) Calculate $(-8) \div (-4)$.

9) Calculate $(10 - 15) \times (-2)$.

10) Calculate $(30 - 10) \div (-2)$.

Fill in the Blank:

11) $12 \div (3 + 3) \times 2 = $ _____.

12) $12 \div 3 + 3 \times 2 = $ _____.

13) $8 + (4 \times 2) - 6 = $ _____.

14) $(2 + 3) \times (4 - 1) = $ _____.

15) $5 \times 2 - (3 + 2) = $ _____.

Calculate:

16) Calculate $|10 - 6|$.

17) Calculate $|-7|$.

18) Calculate $|-3 + 5|$.

19) Calculate $|4 - 9|$.

20) Calculate $|-12 + 4|$.

Answer Keys

1) −8

2) 1

3) 13

4) 0

5) 5

6) −2

7) −30

8) 2

9) 10

10) −10

11) 4

12) 10

13) 10

14) 15

15) 5

16) 4

17) 7

18) 2

19) 5

20) 8

Answers with Explanation

1) When you subtract a positive number from a negative number, you move further to the left on the number line. Therefore, $-5 - 3 = -8$.

2) When you add a positive number to a negative number, you move to the right on the number line. Therefore, $-4 + 5 = 1$.

3) Treat $-(-4)$ as $+4$ since subtracting a negative integer is same as adding its opposite. Therefore, $6 + 3 - (-4) = 6 + 3 + 4 = 13$.

4) Treat $-(-5)$ as $+5$ since subtracting a negative integer is same as adding its opposite. Therefore, $-1 - 4 - (-5) = -1 - 4 + 5 = 0$.

5) Subtract the integers in the given sequence to get the final answer. Therefore, $10 - 3 - 2 = 5$.

6) Use the rule: *(positive)* ÷ *(negative)* = *negative*. Therefore, $4 \div (-2) = -2$.

7) Use the rule: *(negative)* × *(positive)* = *negative*. Therefore, $(-6) \times (5) = -30$.

8) Use the rule: *(negative)* ÷ *(negative)* = *positive*. Therefore, $(-8) \div (-4) = 2$.

9) First, subtract the numbers in the brackets, $10 - 15 = -5$. Now evaluate $(-5) \times (-2)$ using the rule: *(negative)* × *(negative)* = *positive*. Hence, $(-5) \times (-2) = 10$.

10) First, subtract the numbers in brackets, $30 - 10 = 20$. Now use the rule: *(positive)* ÷ *(negative)* = *negative*. Thus, $(20) \div (-2) = -10$.

11) First, calculate within parentheses $3 + 3$, then perform division, and lastly multiplication: $12 \div 6 \times 2 = 2 \times 2 = 4$.

12) Start by performing the division and multiplication before addition. Divide 12 by 3 to get 4, and multiply 3 by 2 to get 6. So, the expression becomes $4 + 6 = 10$.

13) First, perform multiplication 4×2, then addition and finally subtraction: $8 + 8 - 6 = 16 - 6 = 10$.

14) First, calculate within both parentheses $2+3$ and $4-1$, then perform multiplication: $5 \times 3 = 15$.

15) First, perform multiplication 5×2, then calculate within parentheses $3+2$, and lastly subtraction: $10-5=5$.

16) First subtract $10-6=4$, then the absolute value of 4 is 4 since it is a positive number.

17) The absolute value of -7 is 7, because absolute value shows the distance from zero.

18) First add $-3+5=2$, then the absolute value of 2 is 2 itself, because this number is already greater than zero.

19) First subtract $4-9=-5$, then the absolute value of -5 is 5.

20) First add $-12+4=-8$, then the absolute value of -8 is 8.

4. Ratios and Proportions

4.1   Simplifying Ratios

Ratios express the quantitative relationship between two numbers and can appear as fractions, with the word "to," or with a colon. To simplify a ratio is to reduce it to the smallest integers that maintain the original proportion by finding the greatest common divisor (GCD) of the terms involved.

Step By Step   To simplify a ratio, apply these steps:

Step 1   Identify the GCD of the numbers in the ratio.

Step 2   Divide each term of the ratio by the GCD.

Step 3   Express the simplified ratio in its smallest integer terms.

Example: Simplify the ratio 18 : 12.

Solution:

Step 1   The GCD of 18 and 12 is 6.

Step 2   Divide both terms by the GCD (6): $18 \div 6 = 3$ and $12 \div 6 = 2$.

Step 3   The simplified ratio is 3 : 2.

Example: In a class of 32 students, 12 are girls. Find the ratio of girls to boys in that class.

Solution:

Step 1   Find the number of boys: $32 - 12 = 20$.

Step②   The initial ratio of girls to boys is $12 : 20$. The GCD of 12 and 20 is 4.

Step③   Divide both terms of the ratio by 4: $12 \div 4 = 3$ and $20 \div 4 = 5$.

Step④   The simplified ratio is $3 : 5$.

4.2   Proportional Ratios

Two ratios are considered proportional if they express the same ratio or relationship between the numbers they compare. Proportions are typically written as fractions set equal to each other. Cross-multiplication is a common and useful method of solving these equations.

Step By Step

To solve proportions, apply these steps:

Step①   Write the proportion in fraction form, setting two ratios equal to each other.

Step②   Perform cross-multiplication on the two ratios by multiplying the numerator of one ratio by the denominator of the other ratio across the equation.

Step③   Solve the resulting equation to find the value of the unknown.

Example: Solve this proportion for x, $\frac{2}{7} = \frac{8}{x}$.

   Solution:

Step①   Implement cross-multiplication on the given proportion to form the equation $2 \times x = 7 \times 8$.

Step②   Solve for x by dividing both sides of the equation by 2, yielding $x = \frac{56}{2}$.

Step③   Simplify the fraction to find the value of x, which is $x = 28$.

Example: Consider a box containing red and blue balls in a ratio of $5 : 6$ (red to blue). How many red balls should there be if there are 54 blue balls in the box?

   Solution:

Step①   Construct a proportion using the given ratio and the number of blue balls: $\frac{5}{6} = \frac{x}{54}$.

Step②   Apply cross-multiplication to find an equation: $5 \times 54 = 6 \times x$.

Step③   Divide both sides of the equation by 6 to solve for x, resulting in $x = \frac{270}{6}$.

Step④   Simplify to understand that there are 45 red balls in the box, hence, $x = 45$.

4.3   Similarity and Ratios

Similar figures have equal corresponding angles and proportional corresponding sides, allowing for comparisons via ratios. This concept is critical in geometry, assisting us in resolving unknowns by using known measurements.

Step By Step

To determine the length of an unknown side in similar figures, apply these steps:

Step 1   Identify the corresponding sides of the similar figures.

Step 2   Set up a proportion by dividing one pair of corresponding sides to create a ratio.

Step 3   Set this ratio equal to the ratio made from the other pair of corresponding sides, including the unknown side.

Step 4   Solve the resulting equation to find the value of the unknown side.

Example: The following triangles are similar. What is the value of the unknown side?

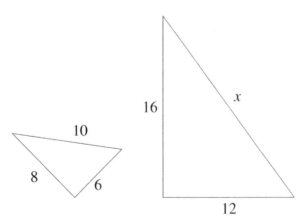

Solution:

Step 1   The corresponding sides of the similar triangles are identified: the sides of lengths 6 and 10 in the first triangle, and the sides of length 12 and x in the second triangle.

Step 2   A proportion is set up using the ratio $\frac{6}{10}$ from the first triangle.

Step 3   The ratio $\frac{6}{10}$ is then set equal to the ratio formed by the second triangle's known side 12 and the unknown side (x):

$$\frac{6}{10} = \frac{12}{x}.$$

Step 4   Solving for x, the equation $6x = 120$ yields $x = 20$. Thus, the unknown side is 20.

Example: Two rectangles are similar. The first is 6 feet wide and 18 feet long. The second is 12 feet wide. What is the length of the second rectangle?

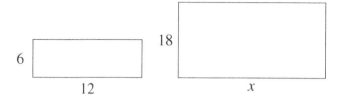

Solution:

Step 1   The corresponding sides of the similar rectangles are identified: the widths of 6 feet for the first rectangle and 18 feet for the second rectangle.

Step 2   The ratio of the corresponding sides of the first rectangle (width to length) is set up: $\frac{6}{12}$.

Step 3   This ratio is set equal to the ratio of the corresponding sides of the second rectangle (width to unknown length): $\frac{6}{12} = \frac{18}{x}$.

Step 4   Solving for x leads to the conclusion that $x = 36$. Thus, the unknown length of the second rectangle is 36 feet.

4.4   Practices

Select One:

1) The ratio of blue to red balls in a bag is $5:4$. What is the simplest form of this ratio?

A) $4:5$

B) $1:1$

C) $5:4$

D) $1:2$

2) What is the simplest form of the ratio $\frac{60}{84}$?

A) $\frac{60}{84}$

B) $\frac{5}{7}$

C) $\frac{5}{14}$

D) $\frac{5}{42}$

3) In a box of fruit, the ratio of apples to oranges is $3:5$. If there are 15 apples, how many oranges are there?

A) 9

B) 25

C) 15

D) 30

4) The ratio of boys to girls in a class is 7 : 3. If there are 21 boys in the class, how many girls are there?

A) 7

B) 12

C) 9

D) 15

Fill in the blank:

5) $\frac{5}{7} = \frac{10}{?}$

6) $\frac{6}{9} = \frac{4}{?}$

7) $\frac{8}{10} = \frac{16}{?}$

8) $\frac{3}{5} = \frac{9}{?}$

9) $\frac{7}{4} = \frac{21}{?}$

10) $\frac{2}{3} = \frac{6}{?}$

11) $\frac{7}{5} = \frac{14}{?}$

12) $\frac{11}{13} = \frac{22}{?}$

Select One:

13) Two similar quadrilaterals have their corresponding sides in the ratio 3 : 1. If the length of a side of the smaller quadrilateral is 6 units, what is the length of the corresponding side of the larger quadrilateral?

A) 2 units

B) 6 units

C) 9 units

D) 18 units

14) Two similar cubes have their edge lengths in the ratio 2 : 1. If the larger cube has an edge length of 8 units, what is the edge length of the smaller cube?

A) 2 units

B) 4 units

C) 8 units

D) 16 units

15) Two similar hexagons have their areas in the ratio 4 : 9. If the smaller hexagon has an area of 36 square units, what is the area of the larger hexagon?

A) 16 sq.units

B) 54 sq.units

C) 81 sq.units

D) 144 sq.units

Answer Keys

1) C) 5 : 4

2) B) $\frac{5}{7}$

3) B) 25

4) C) 9

5) 14

6) 6

7) 20

8) 15

9) 12

10) 9

11) 10

12) 26

13) D) 18 units

14) B) 4 units

15) C) 81 sq.units

Answers with Explanation

1) The ratio is already in the simplest form.

2) Both 60 and 84 are divisible by 12. So, $\frac{60}{84} = \frac{5}{7}$.

3) The ratio of apples to oranges is $3 : 5$. This means for every 3 apples, there are 5 oranges. If there are 15 apples, this is 5 times the amount of apples in the ratio. Therefore, the amount of oranges must also be multiplied by 5: $5 \times 5 = 25$. So, there are 25 oranges.

4) The ratio of boys to girls in the class is $7 : 3$. Since there are 21 boys and 21 is 3 times 7, there are $3 \times 3 = 9$ girls in the class.

5) To find the missing value, cross-multiply and solve for the unknown: $5 \times ? = 7 \times 10$. Solving this gives $? = 14$.

6) Cross-multiplying, $6 \times ? = 9 \times 4$. Solving for ?, we get $? = 6$.

7) Cross-multiplying, $8 \times ? = 10 \times 16$. Solving for ?, we get $? = 20$.

8) Cross-multiplying, $3 \times ? = 5 \times 9$. Solving for ?, we get $? = 15$.

9) Cross-multiplying, $7 \times ? = 4 \times 21$. Solving for ?, we get $? = 12$.

10) Cross-multiplying, $2 \times ? = 3 \times 6$. Solving for ?, we get $? = 9$.

11) Cross-multiplying, $7 \times ? = 5 \times 14$. Solving for ?, we get $? = 10$.

12) Cross-multiplying, $11 \times ? = 13 \times 22$. Solving for ?, we get $? = 26$.

13) By the rule of similarities, the corresponding sides are in the ratio $3 : 1$. So, if the smaller quadrilateral's side measures 6 units (which is 1×6), the length of the corresponding side of the larger quadrilateral is $3 \times 6 = 18$ units.

14) The cubes being similar means their edge lengths are in the given ratio. If the larger cube's edge length is 8, then the edge length of the smaller cube is $\left(\frac{1}{2}\right) \times 8 = 4$ units.

15) The ratio of their areas is the square of their side lengths'. So if the small hexagon's area is 36 square units (which is 4×9), the large hexagon's area should be $9 \times 9 = 81$ square units.

5. Percentage

5.1   Percent Problems

Percentage, or Percent (%), represents a ratio where a value is compared to 100. It is a versatile concept used in various calculations involving discounts, rates, and understanding of fractions, proportions, and ratios.

Step By Step

To solve percent problems, apply these steps:

Step 1   Identify the 'percent,' 'base,' and 'part' within the problem.

Step 2   Choose the correct formula based on what is provided and what is asked for:
- To find the Base, use Base = Part ÷ Percent.
- To find the Part, use Part = Percent × Base.
- To find the Percent, use Percent = Part ÷ Base.

Step 3   Substitute the known values into the chosen formula.

Step 4   Solve the equation to find the unknown value.

Example: What is 35% of 80?

Solution:

Step 1   The Percent is 35% and Base is 80. We are looking for the Part using Part = Percent × Base.

Step 2   Convert the percent to decimal form: $35\% = \frac{35}{100} = 0.35$.

Step 3   Substitute into the formula: Part $= 0.35 \times 80$.

Step 4   Solve the equation: Part = 28. So, 35% of 80 is 28.

Example: 25 is what percent of 625?

   Solution:

Step 1   The Part is 25 and Base is 625. We need to find the Percent using Percent = Part ÷ Base.

Step 2   Substitute the values into the formula: Percent $= \frac{25}{625}$.

Step 3   Simplify the fraction to find the decimal: Percent $= \frac{25}{625} = 0.04$.

Step 4   Convert the decimal to a percentage: $0.04 = 4\%$. Hence, 25 is 4% of 625.

5.2   Percent of Increase and Decrease

Quantifying changes in values using percentages allows us to express these changes relative to an original amount. This proves useful in financial contexts and analytical comparisons such as determining the growth or decline in economic indicators, population numbers, or sales figures.

> **Step By Step**
>
> To calculate the percent of increase or decrease, apply these steps:
>
> *Step 1*   Compute the difference between the new number and the original number. If the new number is higher, the change will be positive (increase); if it is lower, the change will be negative (decrease).
>
> *Step 2*   Divide the difference by the original number to find the ratio of change.
>
> *Step 3*   Multiply the ratio by 100 to convert it to a percentage. The result is the percent of increase if positive, or the percent of decrease if negative.

Example: The price of a shirt increases from $42 to $50. What is the percentage increase?

   Solution:

Step 1   Find the difference between the new and original price: $50 - 42 = 8$.

Step 2   Divide the difference by the original price to find the ratio of change: $\frac{8}{42}$.

Step 3   Multiply the ratio by 100 to get the percentage: $\frac{8}{42} \times 100 \approx 19\%$.

   Thus, the price of the shirt increased by almost 19%.

Example: The price of a table decreased from $75 to $45. What is the percent of decrease?

   Solution:

Step 1   Use the formula for percent change with the new and original price: $45 - 75 = -30$.

Step 2   Divide the difference by the original price to find the ratio of change: $\frac{-30}{75}$.

Step 3   Multiply the ratio by 100 to get the percentage: $\frac{-30}{75} \times 100 = -40\%$.

Thus, the price of the table decreased by 40%. (The negative sign indicates a decrease.)

5.3   Discount, Tax, and Tip

Calculating discounts, taxes, and tips is a fundamental skill in managing personal finances and understanding commerce transactions. By applying simple mathematical formulas, one can determine the selling price after a discount, the added cost due to tax, and the appropriate tip amount for services rendered.

Step By Step   To calculate the discount and the selling price, apply these steps:

Step 1   Identify the original price of the item.

Step 2   Multiply the original price by the discount rate to find the discount amount.

Step 3   Subtract the discount amount from the original price to determine the selling price.

Step By Step   To calculate the tax and the tip, apply these steps:

Step 1   Determine the price of the item or the total bill amount before tax and tip.

Step 2   Calculate the tax by multiplying the price by the tax rate.

Step 3   Calculate the tip by multiplying the total bill amount by the tip rate.

Example: With a 25% discount, Marta saved $60 on a dress. What was the original price of the dress?

Solution:

Step 1   Let x be the original price of the dress. The discount amount is given as $60, which is 25% of x.

Step 2   Set up the equation $0.25x = 60$ to represent the relationship between the original price and the discount amount.

Step 3   Solve for x by dividing both sides of the equation by 0.25, resulting in $x = \frac{60}{0.25} = 240$.

step 4 Conclude that the original price of the dress was $250.

Example: Sophia purchased a new computer for a price of $950 at the Apple Store. What is the total amount her credit card is charged if the sales tax is 4%?

   Solution:

step 1 Identify the price of the computer as the taxable amount, which is $950.

step 2 Calculate the tax by multiplying the taxable amount by the tax rate: $\text{Tax} = 0.04 \times 950 = 38$.

step 3 Add the tax to the selling price to find the final price Sophia needs to pay: $\text{Final Price} = 950 + 38 = \$988$.

5.4   Simple Interest

Simple Interest calculation is crucial in understanding the cost of borrowing money or the profit from lending it. This topic will guide you through calculating Simple Interest using a straightforward formula.

> **Step By Step**
>
> To calculate simple interest, apply these steps:
>
> **step 1** Identify the principal amount (initial amount), p.
>
> **step 2** Determine the interest rate, r, and convert it to decimal form if it's given in percentage.
>
> **step 3** Determine the time period, t, in years.
>
> **step 4** Use the formula $I = p \times r \times t$ to find the interest, I.

Example: Find the simple interest for a $300 investment at 6% for 4 years.

   Solution:

step 1 The principal amount p is $300.

step 2 Convert the interest rate r from 6% to decimal by dividing by 100, which gives $r = 0.06$.

step 3 The time t is 4 years.

step 4 Substitute $p = 300$, $r = 0.06$, and $t = 4$ into the formula:

$$I = 300 \times 0.06 \times 4 = \$72.$$

The simple interest amounts to $72.

Example: Bob borrowed $40,000 from the bank at an 8.5% rate for 3 months. Find the interest Bob will pay on this loan.

Solution:

step 1 The principal amount p is $40,000.

step 2 Convert the interest rate r from 8.5% to decimal by dividing by 100, giving $r = 0.085$.

step 3 Convert the time from months to years: 3 months is $t = \frac{3}{12} = 0.25$ years.

step 4 Substitute $p = 40,000$, $r = 0.085$, and $t = 0.25$ into the formula:

$$I = 40,000 \times 0.085 \times 0.25 = \$850.$$

Bob will pay $850 as interest on this loan.

5.5   Practices

Select One:

1) A store is offering a 15% discount on a pair of jeans that costs 80. What will be the sale price of the jeans?

  A) 12

  B) 68

  C) 108

  D) 95

2) What is 135 as a percentage of 540?

  A) 0.25

  B) 25

  C) 35

  D) 0.75

3) 40 is 80% of what number?

  A) 48

  B) 50

  C) 52

  D) 35

4) A school has 300 students and 60% of them are girls. How many boys are there in the school?

   A) 180

   B) 120

   C) 150

   D) 130

5) If 10% of x is 5, what is x?

   A) 10

   B) 20

   C) 50

   D) 100

Solve:

6) A store sold a desk that originally cost $250 for $200. What was the percent of decrease?

7) A stock increased in price from $20 to $25 over one year. What is the percent of increase?

8) A shirt originally cost $30 was marked down to $24. What is the percent of decrease?

9) A company had 200 employees last year and this year, the number of employees grew to 250. What is the percent of increase?

Solve:

10) Bob bought a TV originally priced at $500. After a discount of 20%, how much money did he save?

11) Anna paid 8% sales tax on her $200 dress. How much did she pay in taxes?

12) You got a 25% discount on a $100 item, and then you have to pay a 5% tax on the reduced price. What is the final price?

13) If you leave a 15% tip on a $40 bill, how much will you pay in total?

14) The original price of a shirt is $45. If it is marked down by 20%, what is the new price?

 Fill in the Blank:

15) If the Principal amount p is $8000, the rate of interest r is 5% and time t is 2 years, the Simple Interest I will be _____.

16) If Lucy deposited $5000 in her bank account which offers an interest rate of 3% per year, the amount of interest she will receive after 8 months will be _____.

17) If the Simple Interest earned on an amount of $5000 over 3 years is $1200, then the annual interest rate is _____.

Answer Keys

1) B) 68

2) B) 25

3) B) 50

4) B) 120

5) C) 50

6) 20%

7) 25%

8) 20%

9) 25%

10) $100

11) $16

12) $78.75

13) $46

14) $36

15) $800

16) $100

17) 8%

Answers with Explanation

1) The amount of discount can be calculated using the formula Part = Percent × Base. Substituting the given values, we get Part = 0.15 × 80 = $12. The sale price will be the original price minus the discount, which is 68(= 80 − 12).

2) The percentage can be found using the formula Percent = $\frac{\text{Part}}{\text{Base}}$. Substituting 135 for the part and 540 for the base, we obtain Percent = $\frac{135}{540}$ = 0.25 which equals 25%.

3) Using the formula Base = $\frac{\text{Part}}{\text{Percent}}$ with 40 as the part and 80% as the percentage, we find Base = $\frac{40}{0.80}$ = 50.

4) First, let us determine the number of girls using the formula Part = Percent × Base which gives Part = 60% × 300 = 180. The number of boys will be the total students minus the number of girls, which is 120 = (300 − 180) boys.

5) let us find x using the formula Base = $\frac{\text{Part}}{\text{Percent}}$, which gives $x = \frac{5}{10\%} = \frac{5}{0.10} = 50$.

6) Percent of change = $\frac{(200-250)}{250} \times 100 = -20\%$. So, the percent of decrease is 20%.

7) Percent of change = $\frac{(25-20)}{20} \times 100 = 25\%$.

8) Percent of change = $\frac{(24-30)}{30} \times 100 = -20\%$. So, the percent of decrease is 20%.

9) Percent of change = $\frac{(250-200)}{200} \times 100 = 25\%$.

10) To find the amount of money saved, multiply the original price with the discount rate. Thus, 500 × 0.20 = $100.

11) To find the amount of tax, multiply the taxable amount with the tax rate 200 × 0.08 = $16.

12) The discount is 25% of $100 which is $25. The new price is $100 − $25 = $75. The tax on $75 at 5% is $3.75. Thus, the final price is $75 + $3.75 = $78.75.

13) The tip is 15% of $40 which is $6. Thus, the total bill becomes $40 + $6 = $46.

14) The discount is 20% of $45 which is $9. Thus, the new price is $45 − $9 = $36.

15) The formula for Simple Interest is $I = prt$. Substituting $p = \$8000$, $r = 0.05$ and $t = 2$ into the formula, we get $I = 8000 \times 0.05 \times 2 = \$800$.

16) Using the simple interest formula $I = prt$, $I = 5000 \times 0.03 \times \frac{8}{12} = 100$. So, the interest Lucy will receive after 8 months is $\$100$.

17) The formula for Simple Interest is $I = prt$. We are given $I = \$1200$, $p = \$5000$, and $t = 3$ years. To find the annual interest rate r, we rearrange the formula:

$$r = \frac{I}{pt} = \frac{1200}{5000 \times 3} = \frac{1200}{15000} = 0.08,$$

which translates to 8%.

6. Exponents and Variables

6.1   Multiplication Property of Exponents

Exponents streamline the repeated multiplication of the same number. Multiplication involving exponents becomes more efficient with certain rules, particularly when working with algebraic variables such as x, y, z, a, b, c, m, and n.

Step By Step

To correctly apply the multiplication property of exponents, follow these steps:

Step 1   When multiplying like bases, add the exponents: $x^a \times x^b = x^{a+b}$.

Step 2   For a product raised to the same power, apply the exponent to both bases: $x^a \times y^a = (xy)^a$.

Step 3   When raising an exponentiated term by another exponent, multiply the exponents: $(x^a)^b = x^{a \times b}$.

Example: Multiply $3x^4 \times 6x^3$.

  Solution:

Step 1   Identify like bases and use the property $x^a \times x^b = x^{a+b}$ to simplify the exponent portion.

Step 2   Combine the numerical coefficients by multiplying them together.

Step 3   Finally, multiply the simplified numerical coefficient by the simplified variable with the exponent to get the answer. Therefore, $3x^4 \times 6x^3 = 18x^7$.

Example: Simplify $(5x^2y^3)^3$.

Solution:

Step 1 Use the power of a product rule $(abc)^n = a^n b^n c^n$ to apply the exponent to each individual factor within the parentheses.

Step 2 Apply the rule $(x^a)^b = x^{a \times b}$ to simplify each exponentiated term individually.

Step 3 Multiply the simplified numerical and variable terms to achieve the final simplified expression.

Thus, $(5x^2y^3)^3 = 125x^6y^9$.

6.2   Division Property of Exponents

Dividing expressions with exponents follows specific rules that make the process easier and more straightforward.

> **Step By Step**
>
> To divide expressions with exponents, apply these steps:
>
> **Step 1** When dividing like bases, subtract the exponents. For example, $\frac{x^a}{x^b} = x^{a-b}$, ensuring $x \neq 0$.
>
> **Step 2** For a quotient of powers with the same exponent but different bases, express the bases as a fraction and retain the common exponent, e.g., $\frac{x^a}{y^a} = \left(\frac{x}{y}\right)^a$ with $y \neq 0$.
>
> **Step 3** If the exponent in the denominator is larger, reexpress the expression so that the exponent is positive, for instance, $\frac{x^a}{x^b} = \frac{1}{x^{b-a}}$ with $x \neq 0$.

Example: Simplify $\frac{18x^4y^2}{3xy^3}$.

Solution:

Step 1 First, cancel the common factor, which is 3, to simplify the expression:

$$\frac{18x^4y^2}{3xy^3} = \frac{6x^4y^2}{xy^3}.$$

Step 2 Apply the division rule of exponents to x^4 and x, giving $x^{4-1} = x^3$, and to y^2 and y^3, giving $\frac{1}{y^{3-2}} = \frac{1}{y}$.

Step ③   Combine the results to complete the simplification:

$$\frac{18x^4y^2}{3xy^3} = \frac{6x^3}{y}.$$

6.3   Zero and Negative Exponents

Understanding the zero and negative exponent rules is fundamental in algebra. These rules allow us to simplify and manipulate expressions involving powers in a consistent manner.

Step By Step   To simplify expressions with zero or negative exponents, follow these steps:

Step ①   Apply the Zero-Exponent Rule: For any non-zero base a, simplify a^0 to 1. Remember that 0^0 is undefined.

Step ②   For a negative exponent, rewrite the expression as the reciprocal of the base with a positive exponent. For $\left(\frac{a}{b}\right)^{-n}$, change it to $\left(\frac{b}{a}\right)^n$.

Step ③   Compute the power of the fraction after flipping (if necessary), which may involve squaring or cubes, etc. Apply exponents to both the numerator and the denominator separately.

Example: Evaluate $\left(\frac{2}{3}\right)^{-3}$.

    Solution:

Step ①   Apply the rule for negative exponents: $\left(\frac{a}{b}\right)^{-n} = \left(\frac{b}{a}\right)^n$. Thus, $\left(\frac{2}{3}\right)^{-3} = \left(\frac{3}{2}\right)^3$.

Step ②   Now, calculate the cube of $\frac{3}{2}$: $\left(\frac{3}{2}\right)^3 = \frac{3^3}{2^3} = \frac{27}{8}$.

Example: Simplify $\left(\frac{4a}{5d}\right)^{-2}$.

    Solution:

Step ①   To simplify this expression, apply the rule for negative exponents, which reverses the fraction:

$$\left(\frac{4a}{5d}\right)^{-2} = \left(\frac{5d}{4a}\right)^2.$$

Step ②   Next, apply the distributive property of exponents over multiplication:

$$\left(\frac{5d}{4a}\right)^2 = \frac{(5d)^2}{(4a)^2} = \frac{25d^2}{16a^2}.$$

Step 3   Therefore, the simplified form of $\left(\frac{4a}{5d}\right)^{-2}$ is $\frac{25d^2}{16a^2}$.

6.4   Working with Negative Bases

When dealing with negative bases, the outcome of raising them to a power depends on the parity of the exponent: even exponents negate the negative base while odd exponents maintain it.

Step By Step

To correctly calculate the power of a negative base, follow these steps:

Step 1   Identify the exponent's parity (even or odd).

Step 2   If the exponent is even and the negative base is in parentheses, the result is positive; if not, multiply the positive result by -1.

Step 3   If the exponent is odd, the result is negative, applying only if the negative base is in parentheses.

Example: What is $(-4)^3$?

Solution:

Step 1   Recognize that 3 is an odd number.

Step 2   Raise the absolute value of the base to the power: $4^3 = 64$.

Step 3   Apply the negative sign because the exponent is odd and the base was in parentheses: -64.

Example: What is -6^2 and how is it different from $(-6)^2$?

Solution:

Step 1   Notice that the exponent 2 is an even number.

Step 2   Calculate the power without considering the negative sign: $6^2 = 36$.

Step 3   Apply the negative sign as a multiplier for the first case: -36.

Step 4   In the second case, raise the base -6 to an even power, resulting in a positive outcome: 36.

6.5   Scientific Notation

Scientific notation is a way to express very large or very small numbers using powers of ten, simplifying calculations and comparisons in science and engineering. In this format, a real number is represented as the product of a number between 1 and 10, and a power of 10.

Step By Step

To convert a number into scientific notation, follow these steps:

Step 1 Locate the decimal point in the original number. If there is no visible decimal point (as in an integer), it is at the end of the number.

Step 2 Decide the new position for the decimal point such that the resulting number m is a digit between 1 and 10; this is done by moving the decimal point to create a number from 1 up to, but not including, 10.

Step 3 Count the number of places n the decimal point was moved to get m. If you moved it to the left, n is positive. If you moved it to the right, n is negative.

Step 4 Write the number as $m \times 10^n$, where m is the number you obtained after adjusting the decimal point, and n is the number of places you moved the decimal.

Example: Write 0.000032 in scientific notation.

Solution:

Step 1 The decimal point is currently after the first nonzero digit, following the zeros.

Step 2 Move the decimal point five places to the right to get the number 3.2, which is between 1 and 10.

Step 3 The decimal point was moved five places to the right, so the exponent n is -5.

Step 4 The number 0.000032 in scientific notation is written as 3.2×10^{-5}.

6.6   Radicals

Radicals represent the roots of numbers, with the notation $\sqrt[n]{x}$ signifying the nth root of x. This means $y = \sqrt[n]{x}$ is the value that when raised to the power of n yields x.

Step By Step

To work with radicals and perform operations, follow these steps:

Step 1   Simplify the radicands (the numbers inside the radical) if possible.

Step 2   Ensure that the radicals have the same index (the root you are taking) when adding or subtracting.

Step 3   Combine radicals by multiplying or dividing if they have the same index.

Step 4   To raise a radical to a power, apply the exponent to the radicand.

Example: Evaluate $5\sqrt{3} - 2\sqrt{3}$.

   Solution:

Step 5   Identify that the radicands are the same (3) and can be combined.

Step 6   Subtract the radicals as you would with like terms to get $3\sqrt{3}$.

Step By Step

To perform multiplication and division on radicals, use these steps:

Step 1   Multiply or divide the radicands when the radicals share the same index.

Step 2   Simplify the resulting radicand if possible.

Step 3   Evaluate the radical if the simplified radicand is a perfect power of the index.

Example: Evaluate $\sqrt[5]{8} \times \sqrt[5]{4}$.

   Solution:

Step 1   Since both are fifth roots, multiply the radicands together to get $\sqrt[5]{8 \times 4}$.

Step 2   Simplify the radicand to get $\sqrt[5]{32}$.

Step 3   Find the fifth root of 32 which results in 2.

6.7   Practices

 **Simplify:**

1) Simplify the expression $2a^3 \times 4a^2$.

2) Simplify the expression $(3b^2)^3$.

3) Simplify the expression $(2xy^2)^3$.

4) Simplify the expression $\frac{5c^4}{c^2}$.

5) Simplify the expression $(\frac{a^4}{b^2})^3$.

Simplify Each Expression:

6) Simplify $\frac{a^8}{a^5}$.

7) Simplify $\frac{7x^5}{x^3}$.

8) Simplify $\frac{b^7}{b^9}$.

9) Simplify $\frac{10a^3b^4}{2a^2b}$.

Simplify:

10) Simplify the equation $(5x^2y^4)^3$.

11) Simplify the equation $(2a^3b^2)^2$.

12) Simplify the equation $(\frac{5x^3}{3y^2})^2$.

13) Simplify the equation $(\frac{3x^3}{4y^2})^2$.

Solve:

14) What is the value of 2^0?

15) How do we represent 5^{-1}?

16) How can we write y^{-3} in standard form?

17) Evaluate 3^0.

18) Evaluate 4^{-2}.

Simplify:

19) Simplify each of the following expressions.

a. $(7b)^{-3}$

b. $(-x)^{-5}$

c. $\left(\frac{1}{2}\right)^{-3}$

Solve:

20) Convert the following number into scientific notation: 45600.

21) Convert the following number into scientific notation: 0.000678.

22) Convert the following scientific notation number back into standard form: 9.12×10^3.

23) Convert the following scientific notation number back into standard form: 1.3×10^{-5}.

24) Multiply these two numbers in scientific notation: 4×10^2 and 3×10^{-1}.

Fill in the Blank:

25) Simplify $4\sqrt{9} = $ _____.

26) Solve for x, $x^{\frac{1}{2}} = 6$ then $x = $ _____.

27) If the square root of x equals 10, what is x? $x = $ _____.

28) Simplify: $\sqrt[3]{8} = $ _____.

29) Simplify: $8\sqrt{3} - 2\sqrt{3} = $ _____ $\sqrt{3}$.

Answer Keys

1) $8a^5$

2) $27b^6$

3) $8x^3y^6$

4) $5c^2$

5) $\frac{a^{12}}{b^6}$

6) a^3

7) $7x^2$

8) $\frac{1}{b^2}$

9) $5ab^3$

10) $125x^6y^{12}$

11) $4a^6b^4$

12) $\frac{25x^6}{9y^4}$

13) $\frac{9x^6}{16y^4}$

14) 1

15) $\frac{1}{5}$

16) $\frac{1}{y^3}$

17) 1

18) $\frac{1}{16}$

19) a. $\frac{1}{343b^3}$

b. $-\frac{1}{x^5}$

c. 8

20) 4.56×10^4

21) 6.78×10^{-4}

22) 9120

23) 0.000013

24) 1.2×10^2

25) 12

26) 36

27) 100

28) 2

29) 6

Answers with Explanation

1) We can use the multiplication property of exponents to simplify the exponent $a^3 \times a^2 = a^{3+2} = a^5$, then we multiply the numbers in front of the variables to get $2 \times 4 = 8$. So, $2a^3 \times 4a^2 = 8a^5$.

2) We apply the rule for powers raised to other powers, so $(b^2)^3 = b^{2\times3} = b^6$, and $(3)^3 = 27$. Hence, $(3b^2)^3 = 27b^6$.

3) Apply the rule where terms together are raised to a power, so $(2xy^2)^3 = 2^3 x^3 (y^2)^3 = 8x^3 y^6$.

4) We use the exponent in the numerator reduced by the exponent in the denominator rule, so $\frac{c^4}{c^2} = c^{4-2} = c^2$. Thus $\frac{5c^4}{c^2} = 5c^2$.

5) When a fraction is raised to a power, the rule is to apply the exponent to both numerator and denominator, so $\left(\frac{a^4}{b^2}\right)^3 = \frac{a^{4\times3}}{b^{2\times3}} = \frac{a^{12}}{b^6}$.

6) Applying the division rule $\frac{x^a}{x^b} = x^{a-b}$, we subtract the denominator exponent from the numerator exponent: $a^{8-5} = a^3$.

7) First, we can retain the coefficient 7 as it is. Then applying the division rule of exponents, we subtract the denominator exponent from the numerator exponent: $x^{5-3} = x^2$. So, the final answer is $7x^2$.

8) Here the denominator exponent is larger than the numerator exponent, so we apply the rule $\frac{x^a}{x^b} = \frac{1}{x^{b-a}}$. Hence $\frac{b^7}{b^9} = \frac{1}{b^2}$.

9) First, we divide the coefficients: $\frac{10}{2} = 5$. Then for the variable part, we subtract the exponents after dividing the same bases. For a, $a^{3-2} = a^1 = a$ and for b, $b^{4-1} = b^3$. Therefore, the final answer is $5ab^3$.

10) We use the power of product rule to simplify the expression. Thus, $(5x^2y^4)^3 = 5^3 x^{2\times3} y^{4\times3} = 125x^6 y^{12}$.

11) Applying the power of a product rule, we get $(2a^3b^2)^2 = 2^2 (a^3)^2 (b^2)^2 = 4a^6 b^4$.

12) For this, we use the power of a quotient rule. $\left(\frac{5x^3}{3y^2}\right)^2 = \frac{(5x^3)^2}{(3y^2)^2} = \frac{25x^6}{9y^4}$.

13) For this, we use the power of a quotient rule. So, $\left(\frac{3x^3}{4y^2}\right)^2 = \frac{(3x^3)^2}{(4y^2)^2} = \frac{9x^6}{16y^4}$.

14) According to the zero-exponent rule, any non-zero number raised to the power of zero is 1. Therefore, $2^0 = 1$.

15) The negative exponent rule tells us to put the base 5 in the denominator and raise it to the positive of the given power. So, $5^{-1} = \frac{1}{5^1} = \frac{1}{5}$.

16) By using the negative exponent rule, we flip the base y to the denominator and change the power to a positive exponent. As a result, $y^{-3} = \frac{1}{y^3}$.

17) According to the zero-exponent rule, any non-zero number to the power of zero equals 1. Therefore, $3^0 = 1$.

18) According to the negative exponent rule, we flip the base 4 to the denominator and raise it to the power 2, so $4^{-2} = \frac{1}{4^2} = \frac{1}{16}$.

19) a. $(7b)^{-3} = \frac{1}{(7b)^3} = \frac{1}{343b^3}$
b. $(-x)^{-5} = \frac{1}{(-x)^5} = -\frac{1}{x^5}$
c. $\left(\frac{1}{2}\right)^{-3} = 2^3 = 8$

20) Determine the factor m between 1 and 10, which is 4.56 in this case. The decimal moves four places to the left, making the exponent 4.

21) The number 6.78 is between 1 and 10. The decimal point moves 4 places to the right, making the exponent -4.

22) The exponent 3 for the 10 indicates the decimal point should move 3 places to the right, thereby converting the number back into standard form as 9120.

23) The negative exponent -5 for the 10 indicates the decimal point should move 5 places to the left, thereby converting the number back into standard form as 0.000013.

24) First, multiply the decimal numbers 4 and 3 to get 12. Then, add the exponents of 10 to get 1. This gives 12×10^1, which need to be converted to 1.2×10^2 to maintain the format of scientific notation.

25) $4\sqrt{9} = 4 \times 3 = 12$.

26) Squaring both sides: $(x^{\frac{1}{2}})^2 = 6^2$, then $x^{\frac{1}{2} \times 2} = 36$. Hence, $x = 36$.

27) The square root of x equals 10, hence $x = 10^2 = 100$.

28) The cube root of 8 is 2 because $2^3 = 8$.

29) Subtracting the numbers in front of the radicals gives: $8 - 2 = 6$.

7. Expressions and Variables

7.1 Simplifying Algebraic Expressions

Algebraic expressions consist of numbers, variables, and arithmetic operations. Simplifying such expressions generally involves combining like terms, which are terms that have identical variables raised to the same powers.

Step By Step

To simplify algebraic expressions, apply the following steps:

Step 1 Identify like terms, which are terms with the same variables and exponents.

Step 2 Combine the coefficients of like terms by adding or subtracting them as indicated.

Step 3 Rewrite the expression with simplified like terms, keeping other terms unchanged.

Example: Simplify the expression: $3x + 4x + 5$.

Solution:

Step 1 Identify like terms: $3x$ and $4x$ both have the variable x raised to the power of one.

Step 2 Combine like terms by adding their coefficients: $3 + 4 = 7$, results in $7x$.

Step 3 Rewrite the simplified expression: Since 5 is a constant and not like any other term, the simplified expression is $7x + 5$.

Example: Simplify the expression: $6x^{\frac{2}{3}} - 2x^{\frac{2}{3}} + 5y^{\frac{5}{4}} + 4y^{\frac{5}{4}}$.

Solution:

step 1   Identify like terms: $6x^{\frac{2}{3}}$ and $-2x^{\frac{2}{3}}$ for x, and $5y^{\frac{5}{4}}$ and $4y^{\frac{5}{4}}$ for y.

step 2   Combine like terms by adding their coefficients: $6-2$ results in 4 for the x terms, and $5+4$ results in 9 for the y terms.

step 3   Rewrite the simplified expression: Combine the results to get $4x^{\frac{2}{3}} + 9y^{\frac{5}{4}}$.

7.2   Simplifying Polynomial Expressions

A **polynomial** is a combination of variables and coefficients structured through addition, subtraction, multiplication, and the variables' non-negative integer exponents. Simplifying polynomials involves combining like terms and ordering them by degree in descending order.

Step By Step

To simplify a polynomial expression, apply these steps:

step 1   Identify and combine like terms, which are terms with the same variable raised to the same power.

step 2   Arrange the combined terms in descending order of their degree (from highest to lowest exponent).

Example: Simplify the polynomial expression $2x^2 - 5x^4 - 3x^4 + 4x^5$.

Solution:

step 1   Combine the like terms. Add $-5x^4$ and $-3x^4$ to get $-8x^4$. The expression now is:

$$2x^2 - 5x^4 - 3x^4 + 4x^5 = 2x^2 - 8x^4 + 4x^5.$$

step 2   Arrange the terms in descending order of their powers to achieve the standard polynomial form:

$$4x^5 - 8x^4 + 2x^2.$$

The simplified polynomial is $4x^5 - 8x^4 + 2x^2$.

7.3   The Distributive Property

The distributive property allows you to simplify expressions by multiplying a single term by each term inside a parenthesis.

Step
By
Step
To apply the distributive property, follow these steps:

Step 1   Identify a single term outside the parentheses and multiple terms inside the parentheses.

Step 2   Multiply the term outside the parentheses with each term inside the parentheses.

Step 3   Simplify the expression by combining like terms if necessary.

Example: Using the distributive property, simplify $4(2x-3)$.

   Solution:

Step 1   Identify the term outside the parentheses, which is 4, and the terms inside the parentheses, which are x and -3.

Step 2   Multiply 4 by $2x$ and then 4 by -3.

Step 3   Combine the products to form the simplified expression: $8x-12$.

Example: Simplify the expression $(-4)(x-5)$ using the distributive property.

   Solution:

Step 1   Identify the term outside the parentheses, which is -4, and the terms inside the parentheses, which are x and -5.

Step 2   Multiply -4 by x and then -4 by -5.

Step 3   Combine the products to form the simplified expression: $-4x+20$.

7.4   Evaluating One Variable

Understanding how to evaluate expressions with variables is crucial for solving algebraic problems. By replacing the variable with a given number and using orderly arithmetic operations, we can find the value of the expression.

To evaluate an expression with one variable, apply these steps:

step 1   Substitute the given value for the variable.

step 2   Perform the arithmetic operations following the order of operations: parentheses, exponents, multiplication and division (from left to right), addition and subtraction (from left to right).

Example: Evaluate the expression $9 + 3x$ for $x = 4$.

    Solution:

step 1   Substitute 4 for every instance of x in the expression: $9 + 3x = 9 + 3(4)$.

step 2   Perform the arithmetic operations while respecting the order of operations. Start by carrying out multiplication, then proceed to addition: $9 + 3(4) = 9 + 12 = 21$. Thus, $9 + 3x = 21$ when $x = 4$.

7.5   Evaluating Two Variables

Evaluating expressions with two variables requires substituting specific values for each variable and then performing arithmetic following the proper order of operations.

To evaluate an expression with two variables, apply these steps:

step 1   Identify the variables in the expression and their corresponding values to be substituted.

step 2   Substitute the given values into the expression in place of the corresponding variables.

step 3   Perform the arithmetic operations following the order of operations (PEMDAS).

step 4   Simplify the expression to find the final value.

Example: Evaluate the expression $3a - 7b$ for $a = 4$ and $b = -2$.

    Solution:

step 1   Identify the variables and their corresponding values: $a = 4$ and $b = -2$.

step 2   Substitute the values into the expression: $3 \times 4 - 7 \times (-2)$.

Step 3   Execute the multiplication: $12 + 14$.

Step 4   Perform the addition to find the final value: 26.

Example: Evaluate the expression $abc + 3ac$ for $a = 3$, $b = -4$, and $c = 2$.

   Solution:

Step 1   Identify the variables and their corresponding values: $a = 3$, $b = -4$, and $c = 2$.

Step 2   Substitute the values into the expression: $3 \times (-4) \times 2 + 3 \times 3 \times 2$.

Step 3   Execute the multiplications: $-24 + 18$.

Step 4   Perform the addition to find the final value: -6.

7.6   Practices

Simplify Each Expression:

1) Simplify the expression: $3x - 5x + 2$.

2) Simplify the expression: $5y + 3 - 2y + 7$.

3) Simplify the expression: $18a + 6 - 4a$.

4) Simplify the expression: $9b - 12 + 2b - 6$.

5) Simplify the expression: $4c + 5 - 2c$.

Simplify:

6) Simplify the polynomial $-5x^3 + 2x^3 - 3x^2 + x - 4$.

7) Simplify the polynomial $4x^4 - 3x^3 + 2x^2 - x + 1 + 3x^3 - 2x^2 + x - 1$.

8) Simplify the polynomial $3x^5 - 2x^4 + x^3 + (2x^4 - x^3 + 1)$.

9) Simplify the polynomial $-3x^2 + 4x^3 + 6x^2 - 2$.

10) Simplify the polynomial $2x^3 + 3x^2 - 1 + 3x^3 + x^2 - x$.

Fill in the blank:

11) $6(n+2) = $ _____ $+12$.

12) $2(4d+7) = $ _____ $+14$.

13) $5(y-3) = 5y - $ _____.

14) $a(3+a) = $ _____ $+a^2$.

15) $b(b+5) = $ _____ $+5b$.

Solve:

16) Evaluate $3x+5$ for $x=4$.

17) Evaluate $2x-3$ for $x=7$.

18) Evaluate $5x+2x$ for $x=2$.

19) Evaluate $4x^2$ for $x=3$.

20) Evaluate $\frac{x}{2}$ for $x=8$.

21) Evaluate $3x-4x+2$ for $x=1$.

Select One:

22) If $a=3$ and $b=2$, what is the value of $2a-3b$?

   A) 0

   B) 2

   C) 3

   D) 6

23) If $a=2$ and $b=-1$, what is the value of a^2-b?

   A) 3

   B) 4

   C) 5

   D) 6

24) If $a=-2$ and $b=3$, what is the value of $ab-b$?

A) -9

B) -6

C) 0

D) 6

25) If $a = 1$ and $b = -2$, what is the value of $3a + 2b$?

A) -1

B) 1

C) 3

D) -3

26) If $a = -1$ and $b = 2$, what is the value of $a - 2b$?

A) -3

B) -5

C) 1

D) 3

Answer Keys

1) $-2x+2$

2) $3y+10$

3) $14a+6$

4) $11b-18$

5) $2c+5$

6) $-3x^3-3x^2+x-4$

7) $4x^4$

8) $3x^5+1$

9) $4x^3+3x^2-2$

10) $5x^3+4x^2-x-1$

11) $6n$

12) $8d$

13) 15

14) $3a$

15) b^2

16) 17

17) 11

18) 14

19) 36

20) 4

21) 1

22) A) 0

23) C) 5

24) A) -9

25) A) -1

26) B) -5

Answers with Explanation

1) Combining like terms $3x$ and $-5x$ gives $-2x$. So, the expression simplifies to $-2x+2$.

2) Combining like terms $5y$ and $-2y$ gives $3y$, and combining like terms 3 and 7 gives 10. Thus, the expression simplifies to $3y+10$.

3) Combining like terms $18a$ and $-4a$ gives $14a$. So, the expression simplifies to $14a+6$.

4) Combining like terms $9b$ and $2b$ gives $11b$, and combining like terms -12 and -6 gives -18, Thus, the expression simplifies to $11b-18$.

5) Combining like terms $4c$ and $-2c$ gives $2c$. So, the expression simplifies to $2c+5$.

6) Combine the like terms $-5x^3$ and $2x^3$ to get $-3x^3$. The simplified polynomial becomes $-3x^3-3x^2+x-4$.

7) Combine the like terms: $-3x^3$ and $3x^3$, $2x^2$ and $-2x^2$, $-x$ and x, 1 and -1 which all simplify to 0. Hence, the simplified polynomial becomes $4x^4$.

8) Combine the like terms: $2x^4$ and $-2x^4$, x^3 and $-x^3$ which all simplify to 0. Hence, the simplified polynomial becomes $3x^5+1$.

9) Combine the like terms: $-3x^2$ and $6x^2$ to get $3x^2$. The simplified polynomial becomes $4x^3+3x^2-2$.

10) Combine the like terms: $2x^3$ and $3x^3$ to get $5x^3$, And $3x^2$ and x^2 to get $4x^2$. The simplified polynomial becomes $5x^3+4x^2-x-1$.

11) Using the distributive property, $6(n+2)$ equals to $6 \times n + 6 \times 2 = 6n+12$.

12) Using the distributive property, $2(4d+7)$ equals to $2 \times 4d + 2 \times 7 = 8d+14$.

13) Using the distributive property, $5(y-3)$ equals to $5y - 5 \times 3 = 5y-15$.

14) Using the distributive property, $a(3+a)$ equals to $a \times 3 + a \times a = 3a+a^2$.

15) Using the distributive property, $b(b+5)$ equals to $b \times b + b \times 5 = b^2+5b$.

16) Substitute $x = 4$ into the expression: $3 \times 4 + 5 = 12 + 5 = 17$.

17) Substitute $x = 7$ into the expression: $2 \times 7 - 3 = 14 - 3 = 11$.

18) Substitute $x = 2$ into the expression: $5 \times 2 + 2 \times 2 = 10 + 4 = 14$.

19) Substitute $x = 3$ into the expression: $4 \times 3^2 = 4 \times 9 = 36$.

20) Substitute $x = 8$ into the expression: $\frac{8}{2} = 4$.

21) Substitute $x = 1$ into the expression: $3 \times 1 - 4 \times 1 + 2 = 3 - 4 + 2 = 1$.

22) Substitute $a = 3$ and $b = 2$ into $2a - 3b$. Then $2 \times 3 - 3 \times 2 = 6 - 6 = 0$.

23) Substitute $a = 2$ and $b = -1$ into $a^2 - b$. Then $2^2 - (-1) = 4 + 1 = 5$.

24) Substitute $a = -2$ and $b = 3$ into $ab - b$. Then $(-2 \times 3) - 3 = -6 - 3 = -9$.

25) Substitute $a = 1$ and $b = -2$ into $3a + 2b$. Then $3 \times 1 + 2 \times (-2) = 3 - 4 = -1$.

26) Substitute $a = -1$ and $b = 2$ into $a - 2b$. Then $-1 - 2 \times 2 = -1 - 4 = -5$.

8. Equations and Inequalities

8.1 One-Step Equations

An equation is a statement asserting that two expressions are equal. Simplifying an equation to find the unknown variable involves performing the inverse operation of what is being done to the variable. One-step equations are those which can be solved by performing a single mathematical operation.

Step By Step

To solve one-step equations, apply these steps:

Step 1   Identify the operation being performed on the variable.

Step 2   Perform the inverse operation on both sides of the equation.

Step 3   Simplify the equation to find the value of the unknown variable.

Example: Solve the equation for x, $x - 6 = -7$.

Solution:

Step 1   Identify the operation: subtraction (6 is subtracted from x).

Step 2   Perform the inverse operation: add 6 to both sides.

Step 3   Simplify to find the value of x: $x = -1$. Therefore, the solution to the equation $x - 6 = -7$ is $x = -1$.

Example: Solve the equation for x, $9x = 54$.

Solution:

Step 1   Identify the operation: multiplication (x is multiplied by 9).

Step 2   Perform the inverse operation: divide both sides by 9.

Step 3   Simplify to find the value of x: $x = 6$. Hence, the solution to the equation $9x = 54$ is $x = 6$.

8.2   Multi-Step Equations

Solving multi-step equations involves combining like terms, rearranging terms to isolate the variable, and using inverse operations to simplify, with a final check of the solution.

Step By Step

To solve multi-step equations, apply these steps:

Step 1   Combine like terms on one side of the equation to group variables and constants.

Step 2   Move all variable terms to one side of the equation using addition or subtraction.

Step 3   Simplify the equation using the inverse of addition or subtraction to isolate the variable terms.

Step 4   Use the inverse of multiplication or division to further simplify and solve for the variable.

Step 5   Check your solution by substituting the variable back into the original equation.

Example: Solve the given equation for x, $3x + 11 = 25 - 4x$.

   Solution:

Step 1   Add $4x$ to both sides to bring variables to one side, yielding $7x + 11 = 25$.

Step 2   Subtract 11 from both sides to isolate the variable term, resulting in $7x = 14$.

Step 3   Divide both sides by 7 to solve for x, which gives $x = 2$.

Step 4   Substitute $x = 2$ into the original equation to check the solution: $3(2) + 11 = 25 - 4(2)$, simplifying to $17 = 17$.

8.3   System of Equations

Systems of equations involve finding the values of variables that satisfy multiple equations simultaneously. We will explore how to solve systems with two variables and two equations using the elimination method.

To solve a system of equations through the elimination method, apply these steps:

Step 1 Arrange the equations with like terms in columns and equal signs aligned.

Step 2 Multiply one or both equations by suitable numbers to obtain coefficients that can eliminate a variable when added or subtracted from each other.

Step 3 Add or subtract the equations to eliminate one of the variables.

Step 4 Solve for the remaining variable in the simplified equation.

Step 5 Substitute the found value into one of the original equations to solve for the other variable.

Step 6 Check the solution in both original equations to ensure they are true.

Example: What is the value of $x+y$ in the following system of equations?

$$\begin{cases} 4x+2y=-8 \\ -2x+4y=-6 \end{cases}$$

Solution:

Step 1 Write both equations with the corresponding terms in columns and the equal signs aligned:

$$4x \quad +2y \quad =-8$$
$$-2x \quad +4y \quad =-6$$

Step 2 Multiply the first equation by -2:

$$\text{Equation 1 (multiplied by } -2\text{):} \quad -8x \quad -4y=16$$
$$\text{Equation 2:} \quad -2x \quad +4y=-6$$

Step 3 Add the modified first equation to the second equation to eliminate y:

$$(-8x-4y)+(-2x+4y)=16-6$$

This simplifies to:

$$-10x=10$$

Step④   Solve the resulting equation for x:

$$x = -1$$

Step⑤   Substitute $x = -1$ into the first original equation to solve for y:

$$4(-1) + 2(y) = -8 \Rightarrow 2y = -4 \Rightarrow y = -2$$

Step⑥   Calculate the value of $x + y$:

$$x + y = -1 + (-2) = -3$$

Hence the value of $x + y$ is -3 for the given system of equations.

8.4   One–Step Inequalities

Inequalities compare quantities using signs to denote less than, greater than, and their respective 'equal to' counterparts. Solving one-step inequalities means isolating the variable through a single operation.

> **Step By Step**
>
> To solve one-step inequalities, follow these steps:
>
> **Step①**   Identify the operation applied to the variable.
>
> **Step②**   Apply the inverse of the identified operation to both sides of the inequality.
>
> **Step③**   If the operation involves multiplication or division by a negative number, reverse the direction of the inequality sign.

Example: Solve the inequality for x, $x + 3 \geq 7$.

   Solution:

Step①   Identify the operation applied to x, which is addition of 3.

Step②   Subtract 3 from both sides of the inequality to get x by itself: $x + 3 - 3 \geq 7 - 3$.

Step③   Simplify to find the solution: $x \geq 4$. Therefore, the solution is $x \geq 4$.

Example: Solve the inequality for x: $-6x \leq 18$.

   Solution:

Step 1   Identify the operation applied to x, which is multiplication by -6.

Step 2   Divide both sides by -6 to isolate x and reverse the inequality sign: $\frac{-6x}{-6} \geq \frac{18}{-6}$.

Step 3   Simplify to get the solution: $x \geq -3$. Hence, the solution is $x \geq -3$.

8.5   Multi-Step Inequalities

Multi-Step Inequalities involve finding the solution to inequalities that require more than one operation. Just as with equations, we simplify and perform inverse operations to isolate the variable.

Step By Step

To solve multi-step inequalities, follow these instructions:

Step 1   Simplify each side of the inequality by combining like terms, if needed.

Step 2   Use addition or subtraction to move all variables to one side and numbers to the other side.

Step 3   Use multiplication or division to isolate the variable.

Step 4   If you multiply or divide by a negative number, reverse the inequality sign.

Example: Solve the inequality $9x + 4 \geq 22$.

Solution:

Step 1   Isolate the term containing the variable by adding 2 to both sides,

$$9x + 4 - 4 \geq 22 - 4 \Rightarrow 9x \geq 18.$$

Step 2   Isolate the variable by dividing by 9, the coefficient of the variable, and remember to divide all terms by the same number,

$$\frac{9x}{9} \geq \frac{18}{9} \Rightarrow x \geq 2.$$

Step 3   The solution to the inequality is $x \geq 2$.

8.6   Graphing Single-Variable Inequalities

Graphing single-variable inequalities involves finding the points on the number line that satisfy the inequality and indicating the range of solutions with appropriate symbols and arrows.

Step By Step

To graph a single-variable inequality, apply these steps:

Step 1   Identify the critical value by solving the inequality if necessary.

Step 2   Plot the critical value on a number line with an open circle if the inequality is strict ($<$ or $>$), or with a filled circle if the inequality is inclusive ($\leq$ or $\geq$).

Step 3   Draw an arrow to the left if the inequality sign indicates "less than" ($<$ or $\leq$) or to the right if it indicates "greater than" ($>$ or $\geq$).

Example: Draw a graph for this inequality: $x \leq -2$.

  Solution:

Step 1   The critical value is -2, which is directly given in the inequality.

Step 2   Since the inequality includes an equal sign, a filled circle is placed at -2 on the number line.

Step 3   We draw an arrow pointing to the left from the filled circle to indicate all numbers less than or equal to -2 are solutions.

$$\overset{\bullet}{\underset{\begin{array}{ccccccccc} -4 & -3 & -2 & -1 & 0 & 1 & 2 & 3 & 4 \end{array}}{\longleftarrow\hspace{6cm}}}$$

Example: Solve the inequality $4 - 3x < -5$ and graph its solution.

  Solution:

Step 1   Solve for x by isolating the variable: $4 - 3x < -5$ leads to $-3x < -9$ thus $x > 3$.

Step 2   An open circle is placed at 3 on the number line as the inequality is strict (does not include an equal sign).

Step 3   An arrow points to the right from 3 indicating all numbers greater than 3 are solutions.

$$\overset{\circ}{\underset{\begin{array}{cccccccc} -2 & -1 & 0 & 1 & 2 & 3 & 4 & 5 \end{array}}{\hspace{6cm}\longrightarrow}}$$

8.7   Practices

Solve:

1) Solve the equation for x: $3x = 21$.

2) Solve the equation for y: $\frac{y}{6} = 9$.

3) Solve the equation for z: $z - 5 = 16$.

4) Solve the equation for w: $w + 8 = 17$.

5) Solve the equation for p: $5p = 40$.

Select One:

6) What is the solution to the equation $2x + 1 = 7 - x$?

   A) $x = 1$

   B) $x = 2$

   C) $x = 3$

   D) $x = 4$

7) What is the solution to the equation $3x + 5 = 2x + 9$?

   A) $x = 1$

   B) $x = 2$

   C) $x = 3$

   D) $x = 4$

8) What is the solution to the equation $8 = 2x - 6$?

   A) $x = 3$

   B) $x = 5$

   C) $x = 7$

   D) $x = 9$

9) What is the solution to the equation $3x - 5 = 4x + 2$?

   A) $x = -7$

   B) $x = 0$

   C) $x = 7$

   D) $x = 2$

10) What is the solution to the equation $5x - 3 = 2x + 12$?

   A) $x = 3$

   B) $x = 4$

   C) $x = 5$

D) $x = 6$

 Solve:

11) What are the values of x and y in the following system of equations?

$$\begin{cases} x + y = 5 \\ 2x - y = 1 \end{cases}$$

12) What are the values of x and y in the following system of equations?

$$\begin{cases} x + y = 10 \\ 3x - 2y = 4 \end{cases}$$

 True/False:

13) $x = 2$ and $y = -1$. Are these the solution for the following system of equations?

$$\begin{cases} x + 2y = 0 \\ 3x - y = 7 \end{cases}$$

14) $x = 1$ and $y = 0$. Are these the solution for the following system of equations?

$$\begin{cases} x - 2y = 2 \\ 4x + y = 4 \end{cases}$$

15) $x = 3$ and $y = 2$. Are these the solution for the following system of equations?

$$\begin{cases} 2x + 3y = 12 \\ 4x - y = 10 \end{cases}$$

Fill in the Blank:

16) To solve the inequality $x - 6 > 9$, we should _____ both sides.

17) To isolate x in $x + 4 \geq 7$, we should _____ 4 from both sides.

18) To solve an inequality with a positive number multiplied by a variable, such as $2x < 10$, we should _____ both sides.

19) To solve the inequality $-3x \leq 12$, _____ both sides and _____ the inequality sign.

Solve:

20) Solve the inequality $3x + 5 > 14$.

21) Solve the inequality $-4y - 3 \leq 5$.

22) Solve the inequality $2x + 3 - x \geq 7$.

23) Solve the inequality $-x + 5 < 2$.

24) Solve the inequality $4 - 3y \geq 10$.

Select One:

25) Which of the following inequality symbols represents "greater than"?

   A) $<$

   B) $\leq$

   C) $\geq$

   D) $>$

26) What does the closed circle in a number line graph of a single-variable inequality represent? (Select one or more options.)

   A) The inequality is "less than".

   B) The inequality is "greater than".

   C) The inequality is "less than or equal to".

D) The inequality is "greater than or equal to".

27) Which direction does the arrow point in a number line graph of a single-variable inequality where $x < 2$?

    A) To the right.

    B) To the left.

28) If an inequality is presented as $x \geq 3$, which of the following is true?

    A) The circle on the number line graph will be filled and Arrow points to the right.

    B) The circle on the number line graph will be open and Arrow points to the left.

    C) The circle on the number line graph will be filled and Arrow points to the left.

    D) The circle on the number line graph will be open and Arrow points to the right.

Answer Keys

1) $x = 7$

2) $y = 54$

3) $z = 21$

4) $w = 9$

5) $p = 8$

6) B) $x = 2$

7) D) $x = 4$

8) C) $x = 7$

9) A) $x = -7$

10) C) $x = 5$

11) $x = 2, y = 3.$

12) $x = 4.8, y = 5.2.$

13) True

14) False

15) True

16) add 6 to

17) subtract

18) divide by 2

19) divide by -3, flip

20) $x > 3$

21) $y \geq -2$

22) $x \geq 4$

23) $x > 3$

24) $y \leq -2$

25) D) $>$

26) C) $\leq$ and D) $\geq$

27) B) To the left.

28) A) The circle on the number line graph will be filled and Arrow points to the right.

Answers with Explanation

1) Use the inverse operation of multiplication, division, to solve for x. Dividing both sides by 3 gives us $x = 7$.

2) The equation $\frac{y}{6} = 9$ involves division. Use the inverse operation, which is multiplication, to solve for y. Multiplying both sides by 6 gives: $y = 54$.

3) The primary operation involves subtraction: $z - 5$. The inverse operation is addition. So, by adding 5 to both sides of the equation, we get $z = 21$.

4) In this equation, the primary operation is addition: $w + 8$. The inverse operation is subtraction. So, by subtracting 8 from both sides, we get $w = 9$.

5) The equation $5p = 40$ involves multiplication. Its inverse operation is division. Dividing both sides by 5, we get $p = 8$.

6) Add x to both sides to give $3x + 1 = 7$. Subtracting 1 from both sides, we get $3x = 6$. Finally, dividing both sides by 3 results in $x = 2$.

7) Subtract $2x$ from both sides to give $x + 5 = 9$. Subtracting 5 from both sides, we get $x = 4$.

8) Add 6 to both sides to get $2x = 14$ then dividing both sides by 2 results in $x = 7$.

9) Subtract $3x$ from both sides to get $x + 2 = -5$, and then subtracting 2 from both sides gives $x = -7$.

10) Subtract $2x$ from both sides to get $3x - 3 = 12$, add 3 to both sides gives $3x = 15$. Therefore, $x = 5$.

11) To solve this system using the elimination method, we aim to eliminate one variable. In this case, we can directly add the two equations to eliminate y:

$$(x + y) + (2x - y) = 5 + 1 \rightarrow 3x = 6 \rightarrow x = 2.$$

Substituting $x = 2$ into one of the original equations to find y:

$$x + y = 5 \rightarrow 2 + y = 5 \rightarrow y = 3.$$

12) To solve this system using the elimination method, we aim to eliminate one variable. Multiply the first equation by 2 and add it to the second equation:

$$2(x + y) + (3x - 2y) = 2 \times 10 + 4 \rightarrow 5x = 24 \rightarrow x = 4.8.$$

Substituting $x = 4.8$ into one of the original equations to find y:

$$x + y = 10 \rightarrow 4.8 + y = 10 \rightarrow y = 5.2.$$

13) We can substitute the values $x = 2$ and $y = -1$ into the equations. They hold true for both equations.

14) We can substitute the values $x = 1$ and $y = 0$ into the equations. They do not hold true for both equations.

15) We can substitute the values $x = 3$ and $y = 2$ into the equations. They hold true for both equations.

16) Since we have $x - 6$ on one side, we need to perform the inverse operation, which is addition, to isolate x. So we add 6 to both sides.

17) Since we have $x + 4$ on one side, we need to perform the inverse operation, which is subtraction, to isolate x. So we subtract 4 from both sides.

18) The inverse operation of multiplying by 2 is dividing by 2. Therefore, to isolate x, we should divide both sides by 2.

19) We should divide both sides by -3 to isolate x. Since we are dividing by a negative number, we also need to flip the direction of the inequality sign.

20) Subtract 5 from both sides to get $3x > 9$. Dividing by 3 gives $x > 3$.

21) Add 3 to both sides to get $-4y \leq 8$. Then, divide by -4 and remember to reverse the inequality to get $y \geq -2$.

22) Combine like terms to get $x + 3 \geq 7$. Subtract 3 from both sides to solve for x, which gives $x \geq 4$.

23) Subtract 5 from both sides to get $-x < -3$. Then, multiply both sides by -1 to get $x > 3$.

24) Subtract 4 from both sides to get $-3y \geq 6$. Then, divide by -3 to get $y \leq -2$.

25) The inequality symbol $>$ represents "greater than".

26) A closed circle on a number line graph indicates that the boundary point is included in the solution set, which means the inequality is "less than or equal to" ($\leq$) or "greater than or equal to" ($\geq$). Therefore, both choices C and D are correct.

27) The arrow in a number line graph points to the left when x is less than the value (2 in this case).

28) The inequality $x \geq 3$ signifies that x is greater than or equal to 3. On a number line graph, this is represented by a filled (or closed) circle at $x = 3$ to indicate that the point is included in the solution set. Additionally, an arrow will point to the right to show that all values greater than 3 are part of the solution set.

9. Lines and Slope

9.1   Finding Slope

The concept of slope is crucial for understanding linear relationships and graphs. The slope quantifies the steepness and direction of a line, which can be computed using two distinct points on that line.

Step By Step

To find the slope of a line, apply these steps:

Step 1   Identify two points on the line, with coordinates $A(x_1, y_1)$ and $B(x_2, y_2)$.

Step 2   Compute the difference in the y-coordinates, which is $y_2 - y_1$ (the rise).

Step 3   Compute the difference in the x-coordinates, which is $x_2 - x_1$ (the run).

Step 4   Divide the rise by the run to get the slope: $\text{slope} = \frac{y_2 - y_1}{x_2 - x_1}$.

Example: Find the slope of the line through these two points, $A(4, -3)$ and $B(1, 0)$.

   Solution:

Step 1   Identify points $A(4, -3)$ as (x_1, y_1) and $B(1, 0)$ as (x_2, y_2).

Step 2   Calculate the rise: $y_2 - y_1 = 0 - (-3) = 3$.

Step 3   Calculate the run: $x_2 - x_1 = 1 - 4 = -3$.

Step 4   Divide the rise by the run to find the slope: $\text{slope} = \frac{3}{-3} = -1$. Therefore, the slope of the line through these two points is -1.

9.2   Graphing Lines Using Slope-Intercept Form

The slope-intercept form, given by $y = mx + b$, allows us to easily plot the graph of a line on the Cartesian plane using the slope m and the y-intercept b.

 Step By Step

To graph a line using the slope-intercept form, follow these steps:

Step 1   Identify the slope m and the y-intercept b from the equation $y = mx + b$.

Step 2   Plot the y-intercept $(0, b)$ on the y-axis.

Step 3   Use the slope m to find a second point by moving vertically and horizontally in accordance with the slope ratio from the y-intercept.

Step 4   Choose additional points if needed by finding corresponding y values for chosen x values using the equation.

Step 5   Plot the additional points on the graph.

Step 6   Draw a straight line through the points to complete the graph of the line.

Example: Sketch the graph of $y = 4x - 8$.

Solution:

Step 1   Identify the slope m as 4 and y-intercept b as -8 from the equation $y = 4x - 8$.

Step 2   Plot the y-intercept by placing a point at $(0, -8)$ on the y-axis.

Step 3   Use the slope to find a second point. With a slope of 4, move up 4 units (rise) and 1 unit to the right (run) from the y-intercept to reach the point $(1, -4)$.

Step 4   Alternatively, select $x = 2$ and calculate $y = 4(2) - 8 = 0$. The point $(2, 0)$ is on the line.

Step 5   Plot the additional point $(2, 0)$ on the graph.

Step 6   Connect the points with a straight line to complete the graph of the line.

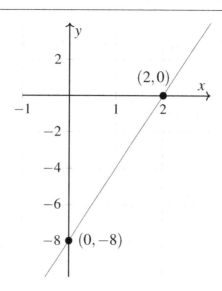

9.3   Writing Linear Equations

To express a linear relationship between two variables, we use the slope-intercept form of a linear equation, which is written as $y = mx + b$, where m denotes the slope and b denotes the y-intercept.

Step By Step

To write a linear equation, apply these steps:

Step 1   Determine the slope m based on the change in y over the change in x between two points, or use the given slope.

Step 2   Identify a point (x, y) through which the line passes.

Step 3   Substitute the slope m and the coordinates of the point (x, y) into the slope-intercept equation $y = mx + b$.

Step 4   Solve for the y-intercept b, which is where the line crosses the y-axis.

Step 5   Write the final equation of the line using the values of m and b.

Example: What is the equation of the line that passes through $(3, -9)$ and has a slope of -5?

   Solution:

Step 1   Start with the slope-intercept form, $y = mx + b$, and insert the given slope of -5, resulting in the equation $y = -5x + b$.

Step 2   Substitute the coordinates of the given point $(3, -9)$ into the equation to get the equation $-9 = -5 \times 3 + b$.

Step 3   Solve for b by performing the arithmetic $-9 = -15 + b$ and then $b = -9 + 15 = 6$.

step 4   Write the final linear equation by replugging the values of m and b into the general form:

$y = -5x + 6$.

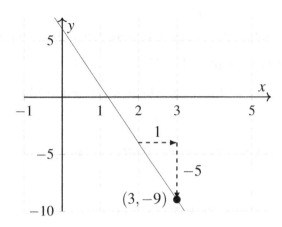

Example: Write the equation of the line that goes through the points $A(-1, 7)$ and $B(3, 3)$.

Solution:

step 1   Calculate the slope m using the formula $m = \frac{y_2 - y_1}{x_2 - x_1}$, which upon substituting the coordinates from points A and B gives $m = \frac{3-7}{3-(-1)} = \frac{-4}{4} = -1$.

step 2   Choose either point $\big(\text{e.g., } A(-1, 7)\big)$ and plug the slope $m = -1$ and the point's coordinates into the slope-intercept form to get $7 = -1 \times (-1) + b$.

step 3   Solve the equation for b to find $b = 6$.

step 4   Finalize the equation of the line by writing it as $y = -x + 6$.

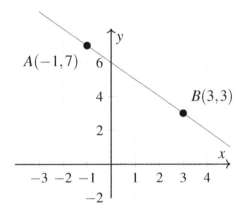

9.4   Finding Midpoint

The midpoint of a line segment is the point equidistant from both endpoints. It can be found using the midpoint formula which averages the coordinates.

Step By Step

To find the midpoint of a line segment, apply these steps:

Step 1   Write down the coordinates of the two endpoints, $A(x_1, y_1)$ and $B(x_2, y_2)$.

Step 2   Apply the midpoint formula: $M = \left(\frac{x_1+x_2}{2}, \frac{y_1+y_2}{2} \right)$.

Step 3   Calculate the average of the x-coordinates (x_1 and x_2) by adding them together and dividing by 2.

Step 4   Calculate the average of the y-coordinates (y_1 and y_2) by adding them together and dividing by 2.

Step 5   Combine the averages of the x-coordinates and y-coordinates to get the midpoint coordinates.

Example: Find the midpoint of the line segment with the given endpoints $(-3, 4)$, $(5, 6)$.

Solution:

Step 1   The coordinates of the two endpoints are $A(-3, 4)$ and $B(5, 6)$.

Step 2   We apply the midpoint formula $M = \left(\frac{x_1+x_2}{2}, \frac{y_1+y_2}{2} \right)$.

Step 3   Calculate the average of the x-coordinates: $\frac{-3+5}{2} = \frac{2}{2} = 1$.

Step 4   Calculate the average of the y-coordinates: $\frac{4+6}{2} = \frac{10}{2} = 5$.

Step 5   The coordinates of the midpoint are $(1, 5)$. Hence, the midpoint of the line segment with endpoints $(-3, 4)$ and $(5, 6)$ is $(1, 5)$.

9.5   Finding the Distance Between Two Points

The distance between two points on the coordinate plane can be determined using the distance formula based on their Cartesian coordinates.

Step By Step

To find the distance between two points, follow these steps:

Step 1 Identify the coordinates (x_1, y_1) and (x_2, y_2) of the two points.

Step 2 Substitute the coordinates into the distance formula: $d = \sqrt{(x_2 - x_1)^2 + (y_2 - y_1)^2}$.

Step 3 Calculate the squares of the differences: $(x_2 - x_1)^2$ and $(y_2 - y_1)^2$.

Step 4 Add the results from the previous step.

Step 5 Take the square root of the sum to find the distance d.

Example: Find the distance between $(5, 9)$ and $(-7, -7)$ on the coordinate plane.

Solution:

Step 1 The coordinates of the two points are $(x_1, y_1) = (5, 9)$ and $(x_2, y_2) = (-7, -7)$.

Step 2 Substitute the coordinates into the distance formula giving:

$$d = \sqrt{(-7 - 5)^2 + (-7 - 9)^2}.$$

Step 3 Calculate the squares of the differences:

$$(-7 - 5)^2 = (-12)^2 = 144 \quad \text{and} \quad (-7 - 9)^2 = (-16)^2 = 256.$$

Step 4 Add the results: $144 + 256 = 400$.

Step 5 Take the square root of 400 to get the distance $d = \sqrt{400} = 20$. So, the distance between point A and point B is $d = 20$.

9.6   Graphing Linear Inequalities

Graphing linear inequalities is a process of finding the solution region on a coordinate plane that satisfies the inequality. Unlike graphing a linear equation, which results in a single line, graphing an inequality shows a whole region.

Step By Step

To graph linear inequalities, follow these steps:

Step 1   Draw the "equals" line using a dashed line for "<" or ">" and a solid line for "≤" or "≥".

Step 2   Select a test point not on the line.

Step 3   Substitute the (x,y) value of the test point into the inequality to determine the solution region.

Example: Plot the inequality $y > -3x + 2$.

   Solution:

Step 1   Draw a dashed line for the graph $y = -3x + 2$ since the inequality is a "greater than".

Step 2   Choose a test point such as $(0,0)$.

Step 3   Substitute $(0,0)$ into the inequality giving $0 > 2$, which is false. Thus, the solution region is not the area containing $(0,0)$, below the dashed line.

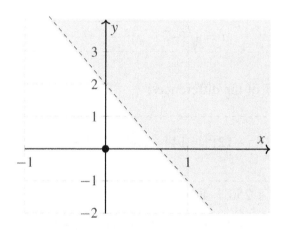

9.7   Practices

Fill in the Blank:

1) Given the points $A(2,4)$ and $B(5,1)$, the slope of the line is _____.

2) Given the points $A(0,0)$ and $B(3,9)$, the slope of the line is _____.

3) Given the points $A(5,6)$ and $B(5,-2)$, the slope of the line is _____.

4) Given the points $A(-4,2)$ and $B(-2,10)$, the slope of the line is _____.

5) Given the points $A(9,6)$ and $B(3,0)$, the slope of the line is _____.

Solve:

6) Solve for y when $x = 3$ in the equation $y = 2x + 1$.

7) Solve for y when $x = -1$ in the equation $y = -3x - 5$.

8) Find the slope and the y-intercept for the equation $y = 4x - 7$.

9) Solve for y when $x = 0$ in the equation $y = -2x + 5$.

10) Solve for x when $y = 6$ in the equation $y = 3x - 2$.

Select One:

11) Given the slope of a line $m = 4$ and a point $A(5,3)$ on the line, which of the following is the equation of the line?

   A) $y = 4x - 17$

   B) $y = 4x + 17$

   C) $y = 4x + 20$

   D) $y = 4x - 20$

12) Given two points $A(-1,2)$ and $B(2,-1)$ on a line, which of the following is the equation of the line?

   A) $y = -x - 1$

   B) $y = -3x + 1$

   C) $y = -x + 1$

   D) $y = -x + 3$

13) The equation of a line is given as $y = -2x + 7$. What does the number 7 indicate in the equation of the line?

   A) The slope of the line

   B) The x-intercept of the line

   C) The y-intercept of the line

   D) A random number

14) Given a line passes through points $(1,3)$ and has a slope of -2, which of the following is the y-intercept?

A) 1

B) −1

C) 5

D) −5

True/False:

15) The midpoint of the line segment with endpoints $(-2,5)$ and $(6,-1)$ is $(2,2)$.

16) The midpoint of the line segment with endpoints $(8,3)$ and $(16,9)$ is $(12,6)$.

17) The midpoint of the line segment with endpoints $(1,-4)$ and $(7,2)$ is $(2,-1)$.

18) The midpoint of the line segment with endpoints $(-5,8)$ and $(-3,6)$ is $(-4,7)$.

Select One:

19) Which number is the distance between the points $(-1,2)$ and $(4,6)$ closest to?

A) 5 units

B) 9 units

C) 14 units

D) 7 units

20) What is the distance between the points $(0,0)$ and $(3,4)$?

A) 6 units

B) 7 units

C) 4 units

D) 5 units

Solve:

21) Solve and plot the inequality: $y \le 3x+2$.

22) Solve and plot the inequality: $y > -2x+1$.

23) Solve and plot the inequality: $y < x-2$.

24) Solve and plot the inequality: $y \ge -x+4$.

25) Solve and plot the inequality: $y < 5x - 3$.

Answer Keys

1) -1

2) 3

3) Undefined

4) 4

5) 1

6) 7

7) -2

8) Slope $= 4$, y-intercept $= -7$

9) 5

10) $x = \frac{8}{3}$

11) A) $y = 4x - 17$

12) C) $y = -x + 1$

13) C) The y-intercept of the line

14) C) 5

15) True

16) True

17) False

18) True

19) D) 7 units

20) D) 5 units

21) Area below or on the line $y = 3x + 2$.

22) Area above the line $y = -2x + 1$.

23) Area below the line $y = x - 2$.

24) Area above or on the line $y = -x + 4$.

25) Area below the line $y = 5x - 3$.

Answers with Explanation

1) The slope can be calculated as $\frac{1-4}{5-2} = -1$.

2) The slope can be calculated as $\frac{9-0}{3-0} = 3$.

3) Since $x_2 - x_1 = 5 - 5 = 0$, the slope is undefined.

4) The slope can be calculated as $\frac{10-2}{-2-(-4)} = 4$.

5) The slope can be calculated as $\frac{0-6}{3-9} = 1$.

6) Substitute $x = 3$ into the equation: $y = 2(3) + 1 = 7$.

7) Substitute $x = -1$ into the equation: $y = -3(-1) - 5 = -2$.

8) The slope-intercept form of a line is $y = mx + b$, where m is the slope and b is the y-intercept. Here, the coefficient of x is $m = 4$ and the constant term is $b = -7$.

9) Substitute $x = 0$ into the equation: $y = -2(0) + 5 = 5$.

10) Substitute $y = 6$ into the equation and solve for x: $6 = 3x - 2$, so $3x = 8$, and then $x = \frac{8}{3}$.

11) We substitute $m = 4$ and $A(5,3)$ into $y = mx + b$ to get b: $3 = 4 \times 5 + b$. So, $b = -17$. Hence the equation of the line is $y = 4x - 17$.

12) First, finding the slope $m = \frac{y_2 - y_1}{x_2 - x_1} = \frac{-1-2}{2-(-1)} = -1$. Then substitute $A(-1,2)$ and $m = -1$ into $y = mx + b$ to get $b = y - mx = 2 - (-1) \times (-1) = 1$. Hence the equation of the line is $y = -x + 1$.

13) In the slope-intercept form of a linear equation $y = mx + b$, the coefficient of x, m, is the slope, and b is the value where the line intercepts the y-axis. Thus, the number 7 is the y-intercept of the line.

14) We substitute point $(1,3)$ and slope -2 into the equation $y = mx + b$, we can find that $b = y - mx = 3 - (-2 \times 1) = 5$. So, the y-intercept is 5.

15) Using the midpoint formula, we find that the midpoint is $M = \left(\frac{-2+6}{2}, \frac{5-1}{2}\right) = \left(\frac{4}{2}, \frac{4}{2}\right) = (2, 2)$, which is the given midpoint.

16) Using the midpoint formula, we find that the midpoint is $M = \left(\frac{8+16}{2}, \frac{3+9}{2}\right) = \left(\frac{24}{2}, \frac{12}{2}\right) = (12, 6)$, which matches the given midpoint.

17) Using the midpoint formula, we find that the midpoint is $M = \left(\frac{1+7}{2}, \frac{-4+2}{2}\right) = \left(\frac{8}{2}, \frac{-2}{2}\right) = (4, -1)$, which is not the given midpoint.

18) Using the midpoint formula, we find that the midpoint is $M = \left(\frac{-5-3}{2}, \frac{8+6}{2}\right) = \left(\frac{-8}{2}, \frac{14}{2}\right) = (-4, 7)$, which matches the given midpoint.

19) Using the distance formula: $d = \sqrt{(x_2 - x_1)^2 + (y_2 - y_1)^2}$, where $(x_1, y_1) = (-1, 2)$ and $(x_2, y_2) = (4, 6)$, we have $d = \sqrt{(4 - (-1))^2 + (6 - 2)^2} = \sqrt{5^2 + 4^2} = \sqrt{25 + 16} = \sqrt{41}$, which is closest to 7.

20) Using the distance formula: $d = \sqrt{(x_2 - x_1)^2 + (y_2 - y_1)^2}$, where $(x_1, y_1) = (0, 0)$ and $(x_2, y_2) = (3, 4)$, we have $d = \sqrt{(3 - 0)^2 + (4 - 0)^2} = \sqrt{3^2 + 4^2} = \sqrt{9 + 16} = \sqrt{25} = 5$ units.

21) This is a less than or equal to inequality, so we draw a solid line for $y = 3x + 2$ and select a test point, such as $(0, 0)$. Substituting $(0, 0)$ into the inequality yields $0 \leq 2$, which is true. So the solution region is the part that contains $(0, 0)$. It is the area below or on the line.

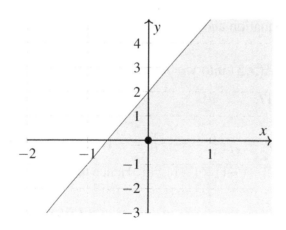

22) This is a greater than inequality, so we draw a dashed line for $y = -2x + 1$ and select a test point, such as $(0, 0)$. Substituting $(0, 0)$ into the inequality yields $0 > 1$, which is not true. So the solution region is the part that does not contain $(0, 0)$. It is the area above the line.

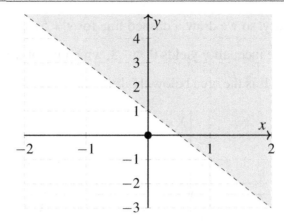

23) This is a less than inequality, so we draw a dashed line for $y = x - 2$ and select a test point, such as $(0,0)$. Substituting $(0,0)$ into the inequality yields $0 < -2$, which is not true. So the solution region is the part that does not contain $(0,0)$. It is the area below the line.

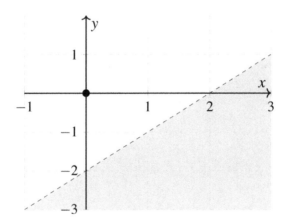

24) This is a greater than or equal to inequality, so we draw a solid line for $y = -x + 4$ and select a test point, such as $(0,0)$. Substituting $(0,0)$ into the inequality yields $0 \geq 4$, which is not true. So the solution region is the part that does not contain $(0,0)$. It is the area above or on the line.

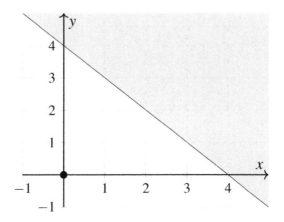

25) This is a less than inequality, so we draw a dashed line for $y = 5x - 3$ and select a test point, such as $(0,0)$. Substituting $(0,0)$ into the inequality yields $0 < -3$, which is not true. So the solution region is the part that does not contain $(0,0)$. It is the area below the line.

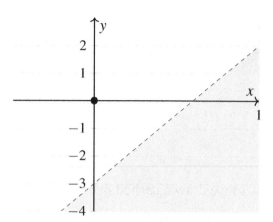

10. Polynomials

10.1 Simplifying Polynomials

A polynomial is an algebraic expression consisting of terms with variables raised to various powers and combined with coefficients. Simplifying polynomials involves combining like terms and arranging them in a standard form.

Step By Step

To simplify a polynomial, follow these steps:

step 1 Identify and highlight like terms within the polynomial.

step 2 Combine like terms by adding or subtracting their coefficients.

step 3 Arrange the terms in descending order of their powers.

step 4 Write the simplified form of the polynomial.

Example: Simplify the following expression: $5x^3 - 8x + 2x^3 + 11$.

Solution:

step 1 Identify like terms: $5x^3$ and $2x^3$ are like terms, $-8x$ is on its own.

step 2 Combine the like terms: Add $5x^3$ and $2x^3$ to get $7x^3$. There are no like terms with $-8x$.

step 3 Arrange the terms in descending order: The terms are already in descending order.

step 4 Write the simplified polynomial which is $7x^3 - 8x + 11$.

10.2   Adding and Subtracting Polynomials

When dealing with polynomials, combining, adding, or subtracting terms is allowed only when these terms are "like" terms – those that have identical variables raised to the same power.

Step By Step

To add or subtract polynomials, apply these steps:

Step 1   Identify like terms (these are terms within the polynomials that have the same variable and exponent).

Step 2   Use the distributive property to remove any parentheses by multiplying the terms outside the parentheses by those inside. Make sure to observe the signs (positive or negative).

Step 3   Add or subtract the coefficients of the like terms to simplify the expression.

Step 4   Write the resulting polynomial, combining all like terms together.

Example: Simplify the following expression: $(2x^2 - x^3) - (4x^3 + 5x^2)$.

Solution:

Step 1   Apply the distributive property to eliminate parentheses: $-(4x^3 + 5x^2) = -4x^3 - 5x^2$. Therefore:
$(2x^2 - x^3) - (4x^3 + 5x^2) = 2x^2 - x^3 - 4x^3 - 5x^2$.

Step 2   Combine like terms by adding or subtracting their coefficients: $2x^2 - 5x^2 = -3x^2$ and $-x^3 - 4x^3 = -5x^3$.

Step 3   Write the final simplified expression by combining the like terms: $(2x^2 - x^3) - (4x^3 + 5x^2) = -5x^3 - 3x^2$.

10.3   Multiplying and Dividing Monomials

A monomial is a single-term expression consisting of a coefficient and variables with exponents. Multiplication and division of monomials involve combining the coefficients and applying exponent rules to the variables.

Step By Step

To multiply monomials, apply these steps:

Step 1   Multiply the coefficients (numerical parts) of each monomial.

Step 2   Apply the exponent rule $x^a \times x^b = x^{a+b}$ for each pair of like variables.

Step 3   Write the resulting expression with the new coefficient and the combined exponents.

Step By Step

To divide monomials, follow these steps:

Step 1   Divide the coefficients.

Step 2   Apply the exponent rule $\frac{x^a}{x^b} = x^{a-b}$ for each pair of like variables.

Step 3   Combine the new coefficient with the result of the exponent operations for the final expression.

Example: Consider the multiplication of the following expressions: $3x^2y \times 7x^5y^4$.

 Solution:

Step 1   Multiply the coefficients: $3 \times 7 = 21$.

Step 2   Use the multiplication rule for the exponents on x: $x^2 \times x^5 = x^{2+5} = x^7$.

Step 3   Use the multiplication rule for the exponents on y: $y \times y^4 = y^{1+4} = y^5$.

Step 4   Write the final result: $3x^2y \times 7x^5y^4 = 21x^7y^5$.

Example: Consider the division of the expressions $12x^5$ by $3x^2$.

 Solution:

Step 1   Divide the coefficients: $12 \div 3 = 4$.

Step 2   Apply the division rule of exponents: $x^5 \div x^2 = x^{5-2} = x^3$.

Step 3   Write the final expression: $12x^5 \div 3x^2 = 4x^3$.

10.4   Multiplying a Polynomial and a Monomial

Multiplying a polynomial by a monomial involves using the distributive property to combine like terms and simplifying the result.

Step
By
Step
          To multiply a polynomial by a monomial, apply these steps:

Step 1 Identify each term in the polynomial.

Step 2 Multiply the monomial by each term in the polynomial individually.

Step 3 Simplify the resulting expression by combining like terms if necessary.

Example: Multiply the expressions $4x(5x + 6)$.

Solution:

Step 1 Identify each term in the polynomial: $5x$ and 6.

Step 2 Use the distributive property to multiply the monomial $4x$ by each term: $4x \times 5x$ and $4x \times 6$.

Step 3 Simplify the expression: $20x^2 + 24x$.

Example: Multiply the expressions $x^2\left(2x + 7y^3\right)$.

Solution:

Step 1 Identify each term in the polynomial: $2x$ and $7y^3$.

Step 2 Apply the distributive property to multiply the monomial x^2 by each term: $x^2 \times 2x$ and $x^2 \times 7y^3$.

Step 3 Simplify the resulting expression: $2x^3 + 7x^2y^3$.

10.5 Multiplying Binomials

A binomial is a polynomial composed of the sum or difference of two terms. When multiplying two binomials, such as $2x - 5$ and $x + 1$, we use the FOIL method to multiply each term of one binomial by each term of the other binomial.

Step
By
Step
          To multiply binomials, apply these steps:

Step 1 Multiply the first terms of both binomials (First).

Step 2 Multiply the outer terms of both binomials (Outer).

Step 3 Multiply the inner terms of both binomials (Inner).

Step 4 Multiply the last terms of both binomials (Last).

Step 5 Combine like terms if necessary.

Example: Multiply Binomials $(x-5)(x+4)$.

Solution:

step 1   The first terms are x and x, so $x \times x = x^2$.

step 2   The outer terms are x and 4, so $x \times 4 = 4x$.

step 3   The inner terms are -5 and x, so $-5 \times x = -5x$.

step 4   The last terms are -5 and 4, so $-5 \times 4 = -20$.

step 5   Combine like terms: $x^2 + 4x - 5x - 20 = x^2 - x - 20$.

10.6   Factoring Trinomials

Trinomials are polynomials with three terms and may often be factored into simpler, binomial expressions.

Step By Step

   To factor a trinomial such as $x^2 + (b+a)x + ab$, apply these steps:

step 1   Identify values a and b that multiply to give the constant term ab and add to give the middle coefficient $b + a$.

step 2   Construct two binomials with the structure $(x + a)$ and $(x + b)$ using the identified values of a and b.

step 3   Verify the resulting binomials through multiplication to ensure they result back into the original trinomial.

Step By Step

   For the special cases of perfect square trinomials and the difference of squares, follow these instructions:

step 1   Recognize the structure of a perfect square trinomial $(a^2 + 2ab + b^2)$ or $(a^2 - 2ab + b^2)$ and difference of squares $(a^2 - b^2)$.

step 2   Factor a difference of squares to $(a+b)(a-b)$.

step 3   Factor a perfect square trinomial to either $(a+b)^2$ or $(a-b)^2$ as per the sign of the middle term.

Example: Factor the trinomial $x^2 - 4x + 3$.

    Solution:

Step 1   Find two numbers that when multiplied give 3 and when added give -4.

Step 2   The numbers that meet these conditions are -3 and -1 since $-3 \times -1 = -3$ and $(-1) - 3 = -4$.

Step 3   Factor the trinomial by writing it as the product of two binomials: $x^2 - 4x + 3 = (x-3)(x-1)$.

10.7 Practices

Simplify Each Expression:

1) Simplify the expression: $3x^2 - 7x + 2 + 5x^2 - 3x + 7$.

2) Simplify the expression: $(7x + 4)(2x - 3)$.

3) Simplify the expression: $4x(2x + 5) - 3x(2x - 4)$.

4) Simplify the expression: $(5x + 3)(5x - 3)$.

5) Simplify the expression: $6y - 7 + 3y^2 - 2y + 5 + 2y^2$.

Simplify Each Expression:

6) Simplify the following expression:

$$(2x^2 + 3x - 1) + (x^2 + 4x - 5).$$

7) Simplify the following expression:

$$(5x^3 - 2x^2 + x) - (3x^3 + x^2 - 2x).$$

8) Simplify the following expression:

$$(x^4 - x^3 + 2x - 7) + (2x^4 + x^3 - x + 3).$$

9) Simplify the following expression:

$$(3x^2 - 2x - 1) - (x^2 - x + 3).$$

True/False:

10) Determine whether the following statements are True or False.

1. $2x^2y^3 \times 3x^3y^2 = 6x^5y^5$
2. $8a^3b^2 \times 4ab^5 = 32a^4b^7$
3. $3m^4n^3 \times 2mn^2 = 6m^5n^5$
4. $2p^3q^2 \times 2p^2q^4 = 4p^5q^6$
5. $3x^4y^3 \times 2x^3y^2 = 6x^7y^5$

Select One:

11) What is the result of multiplying $4x^3$ and $2x^2$?

A) $8x^6$

B) $8x^5$

C) $6x^5$

D) $6x^6$

12) What is the result of dividing $9y^6$ by $3y^2$?

A) $3y^3$

B) $6y^4$

C) $3y^4$

D) $6y^3$

13) What is the result of multiplying $5r^3$ and $7r^2$ and $3r$?

A) $105r^6$

B) $105r^7$

C) $105r^8$

D) $105r^9$

14) What is the result of dividing $12s^8$ by $3s^5$?

A) $4s^3$

B) $4s^2$

C) $9s^3$

D) $9s^2$

15) What is the result of multiplying $6g^5$, $2g^3$, and $3g^2$?

A) $36g^{11}$

B) $36g^{10}$

C) $26g^{10}$

D) $26g^{11}$

Simplify Each Expression:

16) Simplify the expression $3x(4x^3 + 6y)$.

17) Simplify the expression $2y(5x^2 - 3z^3)$.

18) Simplify the expression $5z(7x^2y + 2xy^2 - 3z^3)$.

19) Simplify the expression $7t(4x^3y - 8x^2y^2 + 3z)$.

Solve:

20) Simplify $(x+2)(x-3)$.

21) Simplify $(2x+1)(x-4)$.

22) Simplify $(3x-2)(x+5)$.

23) Simplify $(4x+8)(x-2)$.

24) Simplify $(5x-7)(x+2)$.

True/False:

25) The factored forms of the trinomials $a^2 + 2ab + b^2$ and $a^2 - 2ab + b^2$ are $(a+b)^2$ and $(a-b)^2$ respectively.

26) Every trinomial can be factored using the difference of squares method.

27) The reverse FOIL method allows us to factorize the trinomials.

28) If $a^2 - b^2 = (a+b)(a-b)$, then $ab = 0$.

Answer Keys

1) $8x^2 - 10x + 9$

2) $14x^2 - 13x - 12$

3) $2x^2 + 32x$

4) $25x^2 - 9$

5) $5y^2 + 4y - 2$

6) $3x^2 + 7x - 6$

7) $2x^3 - 3x^2 + 3x$

8) $3x^4 + x - 4$

9) $2x^2 - x - 4$

10) All True

11) B) $8x^5$

12) C) $3y^4$

13) A) $105r^6$

14) A) $4s^3$

15) B) $36g^{10}$

16) $12x^4 + 18xy$

17) $10x^2y - 6yz^3$

18) $35x^2yz + 10xy^2z - 15z^4$

19) $28tx^3y - 56tx^2y^2 + 21tz$

20) $x^2 - x - 6$

21) $2x^2 - 7x - 4$

22) $3x^2 + 13x - 10$

23) $4x^2 - 16$

24) $5x^2 + 3x - 14$

25) True

26) False

27) True

28) False

Answers with Explanation

1) Combine like terms: $3x^2 + 5x^2$ gives $8x^2$, $-7x - 3x$ gives $-10x$, and $2 + 7$ gives 9. So, the simplified form is $8x^2 - 10x + 9$.

2) Using FOIL method: First $7x \times 2x = 14x^2$, outer $7x \times -3 = -21x$, inner $4 \times 2x = 8x$, last $4 \times -3 = -12$. Combining these: $14x^2 - 21x + 8x - 12 = 14x^2 - 13x - 12$.

3) Distributing gives $8x^2 + 20x - 6x^2 + 12x$, then combine like terms to simplify to $2x^2 + 32x$.

4) Using FOIL method, we get $25x^2 - 15x + 15x - 9 = 25x^2 - 9$.

5) Combine like terms: $3y^2 + 2y^2$ gives $5y^2$, $6y - 2y$ gives $4y$, and $-7 + 5$ gives -2. Thus, the simplified form is $5y^2 + 4y - 2$.

6) Combine the like terms: $2x^2 + x^2 = 3x^2$, $3x + 4x = 7x$, and $-1 - 5 = -6$. Thus, the simplified form is $3x^2 + 7x - 6$.

7) Distribute the minus sign and then combine like terms: $5x^3 - 3x^3 = 2x^3$, $-2x^2 - x^2 = -3x^2$, and $x + 2x = 3x$.

8) Combine the like terms: $x^4 + 2x^4 = 3x^4$, $-x - x^3 = 0$, $2x - x = x$, and $-7 + 3 = -4$.

9) Distribute the minus sign and then combine like terms: $3x^2 - x^2 = 2x^2$, $-2x + x = -x$, and $-1 - 3 = -4$.

10) All of these are correctly applying the multiplication property of exponents $x^a \times x^b = x^{a+b}$. Thus, we add the exponents of like variables and multiply coefficients.

11) The multiplication of $4x^3$ and $2x^2$ results in first multiplying coefficients (4 and 2) which give 8 and then adding exponents, which gives $8x^5$.

12) The division of $9y^6$ by $3y^2$ results in first dividing coefficients (9 and 3) which give 3 and then subtracting exponents, which gives $3y^4$.

13) The multiplication of $5r^3$, $7r^2$, and $3r$, results in first multiplying coefficients (5, 7, and 3) which gives 105 and then adding exponents, which gives $105r^6$.

14) The division of $12s^8$ by $3s^5$ results in first diving coefficients (12 and 3) which gives 4 and then subtracting exponents, which gives $4s^3$.

15) The multiplication of $6g^5$, $2g^3$, and $3g^2$, results in first multiplying coefficients (6, 2, and 3) which gives 36 and then adding exponents, which gives $36g^{10}$.

16) Using the distributive property, $3x(4x^3) = 12x^4$ and $3x(6y) = 18xy$. Therefore, the simplified expression is $12x^4 + 18xy$.

17) Using the distributive property, $2y(5x^2) = 10x^2y$ and $2y(-3z^3) = -6yz^3$. Therefore, the simplified expression is $10x^2y - 6yz^3$.

18) Using the distributive property, $5z(7x^2y) = 35x^2yz$, $5z(2xy^2) = 10xy^2z$, and $5z(-3z^3) = -15z^4$. Therefore, the simplified expression is $35x^2yz + 10xy^2z - 15z^4$.

19) Using the distributive property, $7t(4x^3y) = 28tx^3y$, $7t(-8x^2y^2) = -56tx^2y^2$, and $7t(3z) = 21tz$. Therefore, the simplified expression is $28tx^3y - 56tx^2y^2 + 21tz$.

20) Applying the FOIL method, we get: First: $x \times x = x^2$. Outer: $x \times (-3) = -3x$. Inner: $2 \times x = 2x$. Last: $2 \times (-3) = -6$. Combining like terms we get: $x^2 - x - 6$

21) Applying the FOIL method, we get: First: $2x \times x = 2x^2$. Outer: $2x \times (-4) = -8x$. Inner: $1 \times x = x$. Last: $1 \times (-4) = -4$. Combining like terms we get: $2x^2 - 7x - 4$.

22) Applying the FOIL method, we get: First: $3x \times x = 3x^2$. Outer: $3x \times 5 = 15x$. Inner: $-2 \times x = -2x$. Last: $-2 \times 5 = -10$. Combining relevant terms we get: $3x^2 + 13x - 10$.

23) Applying the FOIL method, we get: First: $4x \times x = 4x^2$. Outer: $4x \times -2 = -8x$. Inner: $8 \times x = 8x$. Last: $8 \times -2 = -16$. Combining like terms we get: $4x^2 - 16$.

24) Applying the FOIL method, we get: First: $5x \times x = 5x^2$. Outer: $5x \times 2 = 10x$. Inner: $-7 \times x = -7x$. Last: $-7 \times 2 = -14$. Combining all together we get: $5x^2 + 3x - 14$

25) The factoring process essentially reverses the binomial expansion. Thus, we can see that $a^2 + 2ab + b^2$ factors to $(a+b)^2$ and $a^2 - 2ab + b^2$ factors to $(a-b)^2$.

26) Not every trinomial can be factored using the difference of squares method. This technique only applies for special forms of trinomials.

27) The reverse FOIL method is a process where we factorize the trinomials by finding two numbers a and b that satisfy certain conditions derived from the given trinomial.

28) The equation $a^2 - b^2 = (a+b)(a-b)$ applies universally for all a and b and does not imply that $ab = 0$.

11. Geometry and Solid Figures

11.1 Complementary and Supplementary angles

Angles are a fundamental part of geometry, and knowing the relationship between angle pairs is crucial.

Complementary angles sum to 90° and supplementary angles sum to 180°.

Step By Step

To find a complementary angle, follow these steps:

Step 1 Identify the given angle measure.

Step 2 Subtract the given angle measure from 90°.

Step By Step

To find a supplementary angle, apply these steps:

Step 1 Identify the given angle measure.

Step 2 Subtract the given angle measure from 180°.

Example: Find the complementary angle for 26°.

Solution:

Step 4 Given the angle measure is 26°.

Step 5 Subtract 26° from 90°: $x = 90° - 26° = 64°$.

Example: if $\angle ABC = 32°$, find the angle $\angle DBC$.

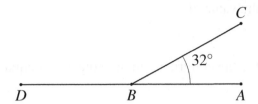

Solution:

step ⑥   Given $\angle ABC = 32°$, identify the angle measure.

step ⑦   Subtract $\angle ABC = 32°$ from $180°$: $\angle DBC = 180° - 32° = 148°$.

11.2   Parallel Lines and Transversals

When a transversal intersects parallel lines, several distinct types of angles are formed, which have unique properties and relationships. By understanding these, we can solve various geometric problems.

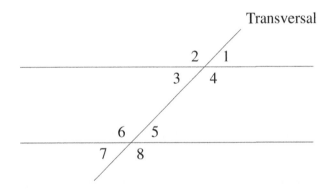

Figure 11.1: Parallel lines intersected by a transversal

Step By Step

To understand the relationships between angles formed by a transversal intersecting parallel lines, follow these steps:

step ①   Identify the congruent angles, which are angles with the same measure, typically angles $1, 3, 5,$ and 7 as one set and $2, 4, 6,$ and 8 as another.

step ②   Determine the supplementary angles, pairs whose measures add up to $180°$, such as angles 1 and 2; 3 and 4; 5 and 6; and 7 and 8.

step ③   Apply these properties of congruent and supplementary angles to solve for unknown variables or angle measures.

Example: In the diagram of Figure 11.1, given that the measure of angle 3 is $4x - 10$ and the measure of angle 5 is $3x + 20$, what is the value of x?

Solution:

Step 1 Set the expressions for the congruent angles' measures equal to each other because they are congruent (angles 3 and 5).

Step 2 Simplify the equation by isolating x. Add 10 to both sides and subtract $3x$ from both sides: $4x - 10 = 3x + 20$ becomes $4x - 3x = 20 + 10$.

Step 3 Solve the simplified equation $x = 30$ for the value of x.

11.3 Triangles

Triangles are fundamental geometric shapes with three sides and angles, and understanding them is crucial in geometry. The angles inside any triangle sum up to $180°$, and the area of a triangle is calculated using its base and perpendicular height.

> **Step By Step**
>
> To understand a triangle's properties, follow these steps:
>
> Step 1 Recognize that a triangle is a polygon with three sides and three angles.
>
> Step 2 Know that the sum of the interior angles of any triangle is always $180°$.
>
> Step 3 Learn that the area of a triangle can be found using the formula $\frac{1}{2} \times (\text{base} \times \text{height})$.
>
> Step 4 Identify that base can be any side of the triangle and height is the perpendicular line from the base to the opposite vertex.

Example: Given a triangle with a base of 18 units and a height of 12 units, can you calculate the area?

Solution:

Step 1 Apply the formula for the area of a triangle: Area $= \frac{1}{2}(\text{base} \times \text{height})$,

Step 2 Substitute the given base and height into the formula: Area $= \frac{1}{2}(18 \times 12)$,

Step 3 Calculate the area: Area $= \frac{1}{2}(216) = 108$ square units.

So, the area of the triangle is 108 square units.

11.4   The Pythagorean Theorem

The Pythagorean Theorem relates the sides of a right-angled triangle, stating that the square of the hypotenuse is the sum of the squares of the other two sides.

Step By Step   To apply the Pythagorean Theorem, follow these steps:

Step 1   Identify the lengths of the two legs (sides a and b) of the right-angled triangle.

Step 2   Use the formula $a^2 + b^2 = c^2$ to set up an equation.

Step 3   Solve the equation to find the length of the hypotenuse c, or the missing leg if c is given.

Example: Right triangle ABC (not shown) has two legs of lengths 6 cm (AB) and 8 cm (AC). What is the length of the hypotenuse of the triangle (side BC)?

Solution:

Step 1   Identify the given sides: $a = 6$ and $b = 8$.

Step 2   Apply the Pythagorean Theorem: $a^2 + b^2 = c^2$.

Step 3   Calculate the hypotenuse: $6^2 + 8^2 = c^2$, $36 + 64 = c^2$, $100 = c^2$, and finally $c = \sqrt{100} = 10$.

So, the hypotenuse BC is 10 cm.

Example: Find the length of the missing side in a right triangle where one side measures 12 cm and the hypotenuse measures 13 cm.

Solution:

Step 1   Identify the known hypotenuse $c = 13$ and the known side $a = 12$.

Step 2   Use the Pythagorean Theorem with the known values: $a^2 + b^2 = c^2$.

Step 3   Solve for the missing side: $12^2 + b^2 = 13^2$, $144 + b^2 = 169$, $b^2 = 25$, thus $b = \sqrt{25} = 5$.

Therefore, the missing side is 5 cm.

11.5   Special Right Triangles

Special right triangles have sides in particular ratios that make calculations easier. The two common types are the $45° - 45° - 90°$ and $30° - 60° - 90°$ triangles.

Step By Step

To deal with $45° - 45° - 90°$ right triangles, follow these steps:

Step 1   Identify that it's a $45° - 45° - 90°$ triangle, which has sides in a ratio of $1 : 1 : \sqrt{2}$.

Step 2   Assign the legs of the triangle a value a, which means both legs are equal in length.

Step 3   Calculate the hypotenuse as $a\sqrt{2}$, completing the ratio.

Step By Step

For $30° - 60° - 90°$ right triangles, apply these steps:

Step 1   Identify that it's a $30° - 60° - 90°$ triangle, which has sides in a ratio of $1 : \sqrt{3} : 2$.

Step 2   Assign the smallest side (opposite the $30°$ angle) a value a.

Step 3   Calculate the side opposite the $60°$ angle as $a\sqrt{3}$.

Step 4   Determine the hypotenuse to be $2a$, twice the length of the smallest side.

Example: Find the length of the hypotenuse of a right triangle if both the other sides are 7 inches long.

Solution:

Step 1   Recognize the triangle as a $45° - 45° - 90°$ triangle because the legs are equal.

Step 2   With both sides equal to 7 inches, assign 7 inches to a.

Step 3   Calculate the hypotenuse using the formula $a\sqrt{2}$: hence $7\sqrt{2}$ inches.

Example: Determine the lengths of the other two sides of a right triangle with a hypotenuse of 8 inches and one angle of $30°$.

Solution:

Step 1   Recognize the triangle as a $30° - 60° - 90°$ triangle due to the given $30°$ angle.

Step 2   Assign the smallest side a value of 4 inches as it is half the hypotenuse.

Step 3   Calculate the side opposite the $60°$ angle using the formula $a\sqrt{3}$: hence $4\sqrt{3}$ inches.

Step 4   The hypotenuse remains at 8 inches as given.

11.6   Polygons

Polygons are flat shapes with straight, enclosed sides, including squares, rectangles, trapezoids, hexagons, and parallelograms. Their properties are commonly defined by the perimeter, the distance around the shape, and the area, the space contained within the shape.

> **Step By Step**
>
> To calculate the perimeter and area of a polygon, follow these steps:
>
> **Step 1**   Identify the type of polygon and its relevant dimensions, such as side lengths, width, length, and height.
>
> **Step 2**   Apply the specific formula for the perimeter or area based on the polygon's type.
>
> **Step 3**   Perform the arithmetic operations to obtain the perimeter or area, simplifying where possible.

Example: Calculate the area of the following trapezoid.

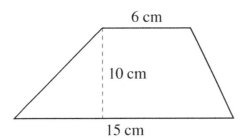

6 cm

10 cm

15 cm

Solution:

Step 1   Identify the dimensions of the trapezoid. Here, $base_1$ (the top side) is 6 cm, $base_2$ (the bottom side) is 15 cm, and the height (the perpendicular distance between the bases) is 10 cm.

Step 2   Apply the formula for the area of a trapezoid, which is $\frac{1}{2} \times (base_1 + base_2) \times height$.

Step 3   Substitute the given dimensions into the formula and calculate: $A = \frac{1}{2} \times 10 \text{ cm} \times (6 \text{ cm} + 15 \text{ cm}) = 105 \text{ cm}^2$. So the area is 105 cm^2.

11.7   Circles

A circle is a simple shape in Euclidean geometry that consists of all points in a plane that are at a given distance from a given point, the centre. Key concepts related to circles include the radius, diameter, circumference, and area.

Step By Step

To understand the properties of a circle, apply these steps:

Step 1   Identify the center of the circle, which is the fixed point from which all points on the circle are equidistant.

Step 2   Understand that the radius of a circle is the distance from the center to any point on the circle. The diameter is twice the length of the radius.

Step 3   Calculate the circumference of a circle using the formula $C = 2\pi r$, where r is the radius and π is approximately 3.14.

Step 4   Determine the area of a circle with the formula Area $= \pi r^2$, where r is the radius of the circle.

Example: Consider a circle with radius of 4 *in*. Use the value of π as 3.14 to find the area of this circle.

Solution:

Step 1   Start with the formula for the area of a circle: Area $= \pi r^2$.

Step 2   Substitute the given radius of 4 *in*., resulting in Area $= \pi(4)^2$.

Step 3   Compute the area using the approximation $\pi = 3.14$, which gives Area $= 16 \times 3.14$.

Step 4   Finish the calculation to obtain Area $= 50.24 \ in^2$. Therefore, the area of the circle is $50.24 \ in^2$.

11.8   Cubes

Cubes are three-dimensional objects with six identical square faces. Each face or side of a cube is equal, denoted by a common side length a. Understanding the volume and surface area of cubes is fundamental in geometry.

Step By Step To calculate the volume of a cube, follow these steps:

Step 1 Identify the length of any side of the cube.

Step 2 Use the formula for volume, $V = a^3$, where V denotes *volume* and a is the side length of the cube.

Step 3 Calculate the volume by cubing the side length of the cube.

Step By Step To calculate the surface area of a cube, follow these steps:

Step 1 Identify the length of any side of the cube.

Step 2 Use the formula for surface area, $A = 6 \times a^2$, where A represents surface area and a is the side length of the cube.

Step 3 Multiply the square of the side length by 6 to get the total surface area.

Example: Find the volume and surface area of a cube with side length 5 cm.

Solution:

Step 1 The side length of the cube (a) is 5 cm.

Step 2 For volume, we use $V = a^3$. Volume $= 5^3 = 125 \text{ cm}^3$.

Step 3 For surface area, we use $A = 6 \times a^2$.

So, surface area $= 6 \times 5^2 = 6 \times 25 = 150 \text{ cm}^2$

11.9   Rectangular Prisms

Rectangular prisms are polyhedra with six rectangular faces, edges that meet at right angles, and three-dimensional measures of volume and surface area. Length, width, and height characterize the dimensions of a rectangular prism.

To find the volume of a rectangular prism, follow these steps:

Step 1 Identify the length (l), width (w), and height (h) of the rectangular prism.

Step 2 Multiply the length, width, and height to find the volume: $V = l \times w \times h$.

To calculate the surface area of a rectangular prism, apply these steps:

Step 1 Calculate the area of the three different sides: length by width (lw), width by height (wh), and length by height (lh).

Step 2 Sum these three areas together: $A_{sum} = lw + wh + lh$.

Step 3 Multiply the total by 2 to find the surface area: Surface area $= 2 \times A_{sum}$.

Example: Find the volume and surface area of a rectangular prism with dimensions: length = 10 units, width = 8 units, height = 6 units.

Solution:

Step 1 The length (l), width (w), and height (h) are given as 10 units, 8 units, and 6 units, respectively.

Step 2 The volume (V) is calculated as: $V = l \times w \times h = 10 \times 8 \times 6 = 480$ units^3.

Step 3 The surface area (A) is: $A = 2 \times (wh + lw + lh) = 2 \times (48 + 80 + 60) = 376$ units^2.

11.10 Cylinder

A cylinder is a three-dimensional geometric shape with circular bases. A key aspect in mathematics is to calculate its volume and surface area.

To calculate the volume and surface area of a cylinder, follow these steps:

Step 1 Identify the radius (r) of the cylinder's base.

Step 2 Measure or identify the height (h) of the cylinder.

Step 3 Use the formula for volume $V = \pi r^2 h$ to compute the volume.

Step 4 Use the formula for surface area $SA = 2\pi r^2 + 2\pi rh$ to compute the surface area.

Example: Calculate the volume and surface area of a cylinder with a radius of 4 *cm* and a height of 10 *cm*.

    Solution:

Step 1   The radius of the cylinder is given as $r = 8$ *cm*.

Step 2   The height of the cylinder is given as $h = 12$ *cm*.

Step 3   Substitute r and h into the volume formula:

$$\text{Volume} = \pi(8)^2 \times 12 = 768\pi \approx 768 \times 3.14 = 2411.52 \; cm^3.$$

Step 4   Substitute r and h into the surface area formula:

$$\text{Surface area} = 2\pi(8)^2 + 2\pi(8)(12) = 320\pi = 320 \times 3.14 = 1004.8 \; cm^2.$$

11.11 Practices

Solve:

1) In the following figure, two lines are parallel. Given that $\angle 1 = 3z - 7$ and $\angle 7 = 2z + 10$, find the value of z.

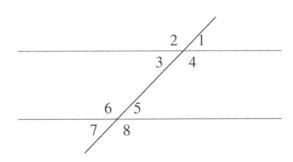

2) If $\angle 5 = 4y + 10$ and $\angle 6 = 5y + 26$, find the value of y.

3) If $\angle 3 = 5a - 3$ and $\angle 5 = 4a + 7$, find the value of a.

Solve:

4) If one of the angles in a triangle measures $90°$, and another measures $35°$, what is the measure of the third angle?

5) A triangle has an area of 50 square units. If its base measures 10 units, what is the length of its height?

6) A triangle has a base of 15 units and a height of 8 units. What is the area of the triangle?

7) If two angles of a triangle are 30° and 60°, what is the measure of the third angle?

8) Given a triangle with a base of 7 units and a height of 12 units, what is its area?

Select One:

9) The Pythagorean Theorem is used for,

   A) Calculating the area of any type of triangle.

   B) Finding the sides of a right triangle.

   C) Determining if a triangle is right-angled.

   D) Both B and C.

10) A right triangle has one leg measuring 12 cm while the hypotenuse measures 15 cm. What is the length of the other leg?

   A) 5 cm

   B) 9 cm

   C) 15 cm

   D) 81 cm

11) If in a right triangle, one leg measures 5 cm and the other leg measures 12 cm, then what is the hypotenuse?

   A) 11 cm

   B) 13 cm

   C) 14 cm

   D) 15 cm

12) In order for the Pythagorean theorem to be valid,

   A) The triangle has to be isosceles.

   B) The triangle has to be a right triangle.

   C) The triangle can be of any type.

   D) The triangle has to have a specific size.

13) The Pythagorean Theorem is written as:

A) $a^2 + b^2 = c^2$

B) $a^2 = 2b^2 - c^2$

C) $a^2 + b^2 + c^2 = 0$

D) $a = \sqrt{2c^2 - b^2}$

Fill in the Blanks:

14) The perimeter of a square with each side of 4 cm is _____cm.

15) A rectangle with a length of 10 m and width of 6 m has a perimeter of _____m.

16) A hexagon with side of 7 m has a perimeter of _____m.

17) A parallelogram with sides measuring 8 m and 6 m has a perimeter of _____m.

Select One:

18) If the radius of a circle is 3 inches, what is its diameter?

   A) 3 inches

   B) 6 inches

   C) 9 inches

   D) 12 inches

19) What is the formula for the area of a circle?

   A) $A = 2\pi r$

   B) $A = r^2$

   C) $A = \pi r^2$

   D) $A = 2\pi r^2$

20) A circle is 8.5 inches in diameter, what is the radius?

   A) 17 inches

   B) 4.25 inches

   C) 8.5 inches

   D) 16 inches

21) If the diameter of a circle is 14 cm, what is the circumference?

A) 12π cm

B) 14π cm

C) 18π cm

D) 20π cm

22) What is the approximate value of π for calculations?

A) 3.2

B) 3.14

C) 3.4

D) 3.41

Fill in the Blank:

23) If a is the length of side of a cube, then the formula for finding the volume of the cube is _____.

24) If a is the length of the side of a cube, then the formula for finding the surface area of the cube is _____.

25) A cube is a _____ object bounded by six identical square sides.

26) The total area of the six identical square faces of a cube is known as the _____.

Select One:

27) What is the formula for the volume of a cylinder?

A) $\pi r^2 h$

B) $2\pi r(r+h)$

C) πr^2

D) $2\pi rh$

28) What is the formula for the surface area of a cylinder?

A) $\pi r^2 h$

B) $2\pi r(r+h)$

C) πr^2

D) $2\pi rh$

29) If a cylinder has a radius of 5 cm and a height of 7 cm, what is its volume?

A) 350π cm^3

B) 245π cm^3

C) 175π cm^3

D) 140π cm^3

30) If a cylinder has a radius of 3 cm and a height of 4 cm, what is its surface area?

A) 42π cm^2

B) 56π cm^2

C) 84π cm^2

D) 112π cm^2

31) Which of the following cylinder has the least volume?

A) Radius = 2 cm, Height = 10 cm

B) Radius = 3 cm, Height = 5 cm

C) Radius = 2 cm, Height = 14 cm

D) Radius = 3 cm, Height = 6 cm

Answer Keys

1) $z = 17$

2) $y = 16$

3) $a = 10$

4) $55°$

5) 10 units

6) 60 square units

7) $90°$

8) 42 square units

9) D) Both B and C

10) B) 9 cm

11) B) 13 cm

12) B) The triangle has to be a right triangle

13) A) $a^2 + b^2 = c^2$

14) 16 cm

15) 32

16) 42

17) 28

18) B) 6 inches

19) C) $A = \pi r^2$

20) B) 4.25 inches

21) B) 14π cm

22) B) 3.14

23) a^3

24) $6 \times a^2$

25) Three-dimensional

26) Surface Area

27) A) $\pi r^2 h$

28) B) $2\pi r(r + h)$

29) C) 175π cm^3

30) A) 42π cm^2

31) A) Radius = 2 cm, Height = 10 cm

Answers with Explanation

1) As $\angle 1$ and $\angle 7$ are congruent, we can equate their expressions and solve for z:

$$3z - 7 = 2z + 10.$$

Solving the equation $z = 17$.

2) As $\angle 5$ and $\angle 6$ are supplementary, their sum is 180. We can equate their expressions to 180 and solve for y:

$$4y + 10 + 5y + 26 = 180.$$

Solving the equation yields $y = 16$.

3) Given $\angle 3$ and $\angle 5$ are congruent, we can equate their expressions and solve for a:

$$5a - 3 = 4a + 7.$$

Solving the linear equation results in $a = 10$.

4) The sum of all angles in a triangle equals $90°$ and another $35°$, then the third angle is calculated as: $180° - 90° - 35° = 55°$.

5) The area of a triangle is $\frac{1}{2} \times$ (base) $\times$ (height). So, the height would be $2 \times \frac{\text{Area}}{\text{Base}} = 2 \times \frac{50}{10} = 10 \text{ units}$.

6) Using the formula for the area of a triangle: $\frac{1}{2} \times$ (base) $\times$ (height) $= \frac{1}{2} \times 15 \times 8 = 60$ square units.

7) The sum of all angles in a triangle equals $180°$. Hence we get the third angle by subtracting the sum of the known angles from $180°$: $180° - 30° - 60° = 90°$.

8) Using the formula for the area of a triangle: Area $= \frac{1}{2} \times$ (base) $\times$ (height) $= \frac{1}{2} \times 7 \times 12 = 42$ square units.

9) The Pythagorean Theorem is used for finding the sides of a right triangle and determining if a triangle is right-angled.

10) Given the lengths of one leg ($a = 12$) and the hypotenuse ($c = 15$), solve for b:

$$\sqrt{15^2 - 12^2} = \sqrt{81} = 9 \text{ cm.}$$

11) Given the lengths of both legs ($a = 5$ and $b = 12$), we solve for hypotenuse (c):

$$\sqrt{5^2 + 12^2} = \sqrt{169} = 13 \text{ cm.}$$

12) The Pythagorean Theorem applies only to right triangles.

13) The Pythagorean Theorem is written as $a^2 + b^2 = c^2$.

14) $P_{square} = 4s = 4 \times 4 = 16$ cm.

15) $P_{rectangle} = 2 \times (10 + 6) = 32$ m.

16) $P_{hexagon} = 6 \times 7 = 42$ m.

17) $P_{parallelogram} = 2(8 + 6) = 28$ m.

18) The diameter of a circle is twice its radius, so the diameter of the given circle is $2 \times 3 = 6$ inches.

19) The formula for the area of a circle is $A = \pi r^2$, where r is the radius of the circle.

20) The radius of a circle is half its diameter, so if the diameter is 8.5 inches, the radius is $8.5 \div 2 = 4.25$ inches.

21) The formula for the circumference of a circle is $C = \pi d = 2\pi r$. The radius in this case is $r = \frac{14}{2} = 7$. So, the circumference is $C = 2\pi r = 2\pi \times 7 = 14\pi$ cm.

22) The value of π is approximately equal to 3.14 for most calculations.

23) The formula for finding the volume of the cube is a^3.

24) The formula for finding the surface area of the cube is $6 \times a^2$.

25) A cube is a three-dimensional object.

26) The total area of the six identical squares of a cube is known as the Surface Area.

27) The volume of a cylinder is given by the formula $\pi r^2 h$, where r is the radius and h is the height.

28) The surface area of a cylinder is given by the formula $2\pi r(r+h)$, where r is the radius and h is the height.

29) The volume of the cylinder can be calculated using the formula $\pi r^2 h$. Substituting the given values, we get $\pi(5)^2 \times 7 = 175\pi$ cm^3.

30) The surface area of the cylinder can be calculated using the formula $2\pi r(r+h)$. Substituting the given values, we get $2\pi(3)(3+4) = 42\pi$ cm^2.

31) By calculating the volume for each of the cylinders using $\pi r^2 h$, we find that the first cylinder has the smallest volume.

12. Statistics

12.1 Mean, Median, Mode, and Range of the Given Data

The topic covers the measures of central tendency and dispersion for a data set: mean, median, mode, and range. The mean is the average, the median is the middle value when the data is in order, the mode is the most frequent value, and the range is the difference between the highest and lowest values.

Step By Step

To calculate the mean, median, mode, and range of a data set, follow these steps:

Step 1 Add up all the data values to find the sum.

Step 2 Divide the sum by the total number of data entries to find the mean.

Step 3 Identify the value that occurs most frequently for the mode. If two or more values tie for most frequent, the set is bimodal or multimodal, respectively.

Step 4 Arrange the data in ascending order and find the middle value(s) to determine the median. If there is an even number of data entries, calculate the average of the two middle numbers.

Step 5 Subtract the smallest data value from the largest to calculate the range.

Example: Calculate the mean, mode, median, and range of the following set of numbers:

$$4,7,9,7,9,4,1,4,4,8.$$

Solution:

Step 1   Calculate the sum of the numbers: $4+7+9+7+9+4+1+4+4+8 = 57$.

Step 2   Divide the sum by the count of numbers: $\frac{57}{10} = 5.7$. The mean is 5.7.

Step 3   The number 4 appears four times, more than any other number, so the mode is 4.

Step 4   Put numbers in ascending order: $1,4,4,4,4,7,7,8,9,9$. The median is the average of the 5th and 6th numbers: $\frac{4+7}{2} = 5.5$.

Step 5   Subtract the smallest number (1) from the largest (9) to get the range: $9-1 = 8$.

12.2   Pie Graph

Pie Graphs, or Pie Charts, are circular charts divided into slices to represent the relative sizes of various categories. They are an effective way to visualize the proportional distribution of different categories within a whole set.

Step By Step

To create a pie chart, apply these steps for the percentage method:

Step 1   Identify the different categories you wish to represent.

Step 2   Determine the number of instances in each category.

Step 3   Calculate the total number of instances across all categories.

Step 4   Calculate the percentage each category represents out of the total.

Step 5   Draw a circle and divide it into sectors proportional to the percentages.

For the degree method to create a pie chart, follow these instructions:

Step 1   Identify the different categories you wish to represent.

Step 2   Determine the number of instances in each category.

Step 3   Calculate the total number of instances across all categories.

Step 4   Calculate the angle of each sector in degrees for each category.

Step 5   Draw a circle and divide it into sectors using the angles calculated.

Example: The following pie chart represents the distribution of various subject's book in a library. What is the number of Mathematics books in the library considering the total number of books to be 750?

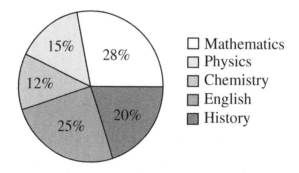

Solution:

Step 1   Identify that the category in question is Mathematics books.

Step 2   Note that the percentage of Mathematics books is 28% as given in the chart.

Step 3   Calculate the number of Mathematics books by taking 28% of the total number of books (750).

Step 4   Perform the calculation: $28\% \times 750 = 0.28 \times 750 = 210$.

Step 5   Conclude that there are 210 Mathematics books in the library.

12.3   Probability Problems

Probability quantifies how likely it is for a particular event to occur within a set of possible outcomes. Understanding how to calculate probability is essential for a variety of scenarios.

To calculate the probability of an event, apply these steps:

Step 1   Identify the total number of possible outcomes in the experiment.

Step 2   Determine the number of ways the desired event can occur.

Step 3   Use the probability formula $P(E) = \frac{\text{number of desired outcomes}}{\text{number of total outcomes}}$ to calculate the probability.

Step 4   Simplify the fraction if necessary or convert it to a decimal or percentage, depending on the context of the problem.

Example: Sara's trick–or–treat bag contains 13 pieces of chocolate, 17 suckers, 18 pieces of gum, and 20 pieces of licorice. If she randomly pulls a piece of candy from her bag, what is the probability of her pulling out a piece of sucker?

  Solution:

Step 1   Calculate the total number of pieces of candy in the bag by adding them together: $13 + 17 + 18 + 20 = 68$.

Step 2   Identify the number of suckers in the bag: 17.

Step 3   Apply the probability formula:

$$P(\text{sucker}) = \frac{\text{number of suckers}}{\text{total number of pieces of candy}} = \frac{17}{68}.$$

Step 4   Simplify the fraction to find the probability of pulling out a sucker: $\frac{17}{68} = \frac{1}{4}$. This can be expressed as a 25% chance.

12.4   Permutations and Combinations

Permutations and combinations are fundamental concepts in combinatorics, dealing with the arrangement and selection of objects. They utilize factorials to calculate the number of possible orderings or groupings.

Step
By
Step   To calculate permutations or combinations, apply the following steps:

Step 1   Understand the problem and determine whether order is important (permutations) or not (combinations).

Step 2   Identify the total number of objects (n) and the number of objects to choose or arrange (r).

Step 3   Use the permutations formula $P(n,r) = \frac{n!}{(n-r)!}$ if order matters, or the combinations formula $C(n,r) = \frac{n!}{r!(n-r)!}$ if order does not matter.

Step 4   Solve the factorial expressions and compute the result.

Example: How many ways can the first, second, third and fourth place be awarded among twelve competitive swimmers?

Solution:

Step 1   This is a permutations problem because the order of awarding matters.

Step 2   Here, $n = 12$ (total swimmers) and $r = 4$ (places to award).

Step 3   Apply the permutations formula:

$$\frac{n!}{(n-r)!} = \frac{12!}{(12-4)!} = \frac{12!}{8!}.$$

Step 4   Simplify and calculate the result:

$$\frac{12 \times 11 \times 10 \times 9 \times 8!}{8!} = 12 \times 11 \times 10 \times 9 = 11880.$$

So, there are 11880 ways to award the first, second, third and fourth place among the twelve swimmers.

Example: In a class of 17 students, six students need to be selected to form a music band for the school competition. How many ways can these students be selected?

Solution:

Step 1   This problem is about combinations since the order does not matter.

Step 2   Here, $n = 17$ (total students) and $r = 6$ (students to select).

step 3   Apply the combinations formula:

$$\frac{n!}{r!(n-r)!} = \frac{17!}{6!(17-6)!} = \frac{17!}{6! \times 11!}.$$

step 4   Simplify and calculate the result:

$$\frac{17 \times 16 \times 15 \times 14 \times 13 \times 12 \times 11!}{6! \times 11!} = \frac{17 \times 16 \times 15 \times 14 \times 13 \times 12}{6 \times 5 \times 4 \times 3 \times 2} = 12376.$$

Therefore, there are 12376 ways to select six students from a class of 17.

12.5   Practices

 **Select One:**

1) Given the data set {8, 5, 12, 7, 10, 8, 8}, which of the following is the mode of the data?

   A) 5

   B) 8

   C) 10

   D) 12

2) The mean of a data set is 15 and the range is 10. The lowest number is 8. What is the highest number?

   A) 10

   B) 15

   C) 18

   D) 25

3) The median of a data set 4, 6, x, 9, 14 is 9. What is the value of x?

   A) 4

   B) 6

   C) 9

   D) 14

4) Which of these can never be negative?

   A) Mean

   B) Median

C) Mode

D) Range

5) In a set of test scores, the mode is 95 and the median is 85. What can be concluded about the scores?

   A) More students scored 95 than any other score.

   B) The average score is 85.

   C) Half of the students scored less than 85.

   D) A and C

   E) A and B

Fill in the Blank:

6) The angles in a pie chart add up to _____ degrees.

7) If a pie chart is representing percentages, all the proportions should sum up to _____.

8) A sector subtending 45 degrees at the center of a pie chart corresponds to _____ percent of the total.

9) In a pie chart depicting grades of 150 students, the number of students who received a B grade is represented by a sector subtending an angle of 108 degrees. The number of students receiving a B grade is _____.

10) In a pie chart, each sector corresponds to _____ of data.

Solve:

11) In a class of 30 students, 15 are boys and 15 are girls. If a student is picked at random, constitute the equation for the probability of picking a girl and solve.

12) A bag contains 5 green balls, 3 red balls, and 2 yellow balls. If one ball is picked at random, constitute the equation for the probability of not picking a red ball and solve.

13) A man has 4 shirts: 2 are red, 1 is blue, and 1 is green. He chooses a shirt at random. Write and solve the equation for the probability that he chooses a red shirt.

14) Write and solve an equation for the probability for getting a total 7 when rolling two dice.

15) A box contains 4 black balls, 8 white balls, and 3 green balls. If a ball is drawn at random, write and solve the equation for the probability that the ball drawn is not black.

Fill in the Blank:

16) In a room with 5 people, there are _____ ways to choose 2 people to form a committee.

17) In a group of 12 people, there are _____ ways to arrange them in a row for a picture.

18) In a bag with 8 different colored balls, there are _____ ways to choose 3 balls without replacement.

19) For a set of 7 letters, there are _____ ways to arrange 4 of those letters into words with no repetition.

20) If you have a 4 digit lock where each digit can be 0-9, there are _____ possible combinations if repetition is allowed.

Answer Keys

1) B) 8

2) C) 18

3) C) 9

4) D) Range

5) D) A and C

6) 360

7) 100%

8) 12.5%

9) 45

10) A category

11) 0.5

12) 0.7

13) 0.5

14) 0.167

15) 0.733

16) 10

17) 479,001,600

18) 56

19) 840

20) 10,000

Answers with Explanation

1) The mode of the data set is the number that appears most frequently. The number 8 appears three times, more often than any other number in the set, so it is the mode.

2) The range is the difference between the highest and the lowest numbers. So, the highest number is the lowest number (8) plus the range (10), which equals 18.

3) The median of a data set is the middle number when the data set is arranged in ascending order. Therefore, x must be 9 for the middle number to be 9.

4) The range is a measure of dispersion or variation and it is the difference between the highest and the lowest values in a set, it can never be negative.

5) The mode indicates the score that appeared most, which is 95. The median being 85 indicates that half of the scores fell below 85.

6) A pie chart is a circle and the sum of the angles in a circle is 360 degrees.

7) The entire pie chart stands for 100%.

8) Percentage $= \frac{45}{360} \times 100\% = 12.5\%$.

9) The proportion of students who received a B grade $= \frac{108}{360} = 0.3$. So the number of students $= 0.3 \times 150 = 45$.

10) Each sector in a pie chart corresponds to a category of data.

11) Out of a total of 30 students, 15 are girls. Therefore, the equation for the probability of picking a girl is $P(G) = \frac{\text{Girls}}{\text{Total}}$. So, $P(G) = \frac{15}{30} = 0.5$

12) Out of a total of 10 balls, 7 are not red. Therefore, the equation for the probability of not picking a red ball is $P(\sim R) = \frac{\text{Not Red}}{\text{Total}}$. So, $P(\sim R) = \frac{7}{10} = 0.7$

13) Out of the total 4 shirts, 2 are red. Therefore, the equation for the probability of choosing a red shirt is $P(R) = \frac{\text{Red shirts}}{\text{Total shirts}}$. So, $P(R) = \frac{2}{4} = 0.5$

14) There are 6 total outcomes (1 and 6, 2 and 5, 3 and 4, 4 and 3, 5 and 2, 6 and 1) out of 36 total outcomes that sum to 7. Therefore, the equation for this probability is $P(7) = \frac{\text{Outcomes of 7}}{\text{Total outcomes}}$. So, $P(7) = \frac{6}{36} = 0.167$

15) Of the total 15 balls, 11 are not black. Therefore, the equation for the probability of not drawing a black ball is $P(\sim B) = \frac{\text{Not Black}}{\text{Total}}$. So, $P(\sim B) = \frac{11}{15} = 0.733$.

16) This is a combination without repetition problem: $C(n,r) = \frac{n!}{r!(n-r)!}$. Substituting $n = 5$ and $r = 2$, we get $C(5,2) = \frac{5!}{2!(5-2)!} = 10$.

17) This is a permutation without repetition problem: $P(n) = n!$. As there are 12 people, there are $12! = 479,001,600$ ways to arrange them.

18) This is a combination without repetition problem: $C(n,r) = \frac{n!}{r!(n-r)!}$. Substituting $n = 8$ and $r = 3$, we get $C(8,3) = \frac{8!}{3!(8-3)!} = 56$.

19) This is a permutation without repetition problem: $P(n,r) = \frac{n!}{(n-r)!}$. Substituting $n = 7$ and $r = 4$, we get $P(7,4) = \frac{7!}{(7-4)!} = 840$.

20) There are 10 options (0 through 9) for each of the 4 digits. Since repetition is allowed, this is a permutation problem with repetition, giving us $10^4 = 10,000$ possibilities.

13. Functions Operations

13.1 Function Notation and Evaluation

Functions are core to understanding algebra and calculus. They relate inputs to outputs in a consistent way and can be notated with symbols like $f(x)$.

Step By Step

To evaluate a function, apply these steps:

Step 1   Identify the function notation and the input value.

Step 2   Substitute the input value into the function in place of the variable.

Step 3   Simplify the expression to find the output.

Example: Evaluate: $f(x) = 2x + 5$, find $f(3)$.

    Solution:

Step 1   We identify the function $f(x) = 2x + 5$ and the input value 3.

Step 2   Substitute 3 for x in the function: $f(3) = 2(3) + 5$.

Step 3   Simplify the expression: $f(3) = 11$.

Example: Evaluate: $w(x) = 2x - 4$, find $w(5)$.

    Solution:

Step 1   We identify the function $w(x) = 2x - 4$ and the input value 5.

Step 2   Substitute 5 for x in the function: $w(5) = 2(5) - 4$.

Step 3   Simplify the expression to find the output: $w(5) = 6$.

13.2 Adding and Subtracting Functions

Just like we can add and subtract numbers and expressions, we can also add or subtract functions. This involves adding or subtracting the functions directly to create a new function.

Step By Step

To add or subtract functions, apply these steps:

Step 1   Write the functions $f(x)$ and $g(x)$ explicitly.

Step 2   Add or subtract the functions directly.

Step 3   Simplify the resulting expression to find the new function $(f \pm g)(x)$.

Example: Given $g(x) = x - 5$ and $f(x) = 3x + 4$, find $(g + f)(x)$.

Solution:

Step 1   Write $g(x) = x - 5$ and $f(x) = 3x + 4$.

Step 2   Add the functions: $(g + f)(x) = (x - 5) + (3x + 4)$.

Step 3   Simplify the expression: $(g + f)(x) = 4x - 1$.

Example: Given $h(x) = 2x + 5$ and $k(x) = -4x - 3$, find $(h - k)(x)$.

Solution:

Step 1   Write $h(x) = 2x + 5$ and $k(x) = -4x - 3$.

Step 2   Subtract the functions: $(h - k)(x) = (2x + 5) - (-4x - 3)$.

Step 3   Simplify the expression: $(h - k)(x) = 6x + 8$.

13.3 Multiplying and Dividing Functions

When we have two functions $f(x)$ and $g(x)$, we can combine them through multiplication or division to get a new function. The multiplication is expressed as $(f \cdot g)(x) = f(x) \cdot g(x)$, while division is $\left(\frac{f}{g}\right)(x) = \frac{f(x)}{g(x)}$, provided that $g(x) \neq 0$.

Step By Step

To multiply functions, apply these steps:

Step 1   Write down the expressions for both functions $f(x)$ and $g(x)$.

Step 2   Multiply the expressions $f(x) \cdot g(x)$ to find $(f \cdot g)(x)$.

Step 3   Simplify the product to get the final expression for $(f \cdot g)(x)$.

Step By Step

To divide functions, apply these steps:

Step 1   Write down the expressions for both functions $f(x)$ and $g(x)$, ensuring $g(x) \neq 0$.

Step 2   Divide $f(x)$ by $g(x)$ to find $\left(\frac{f}{g}\right)(x)$.

Step 3   Simplify the quotient and note the values for which $g(x) = 0$, as the function is undefined for those values.

Example: If $g(x) = x + 2$ and $f(x) = x + 3$, compute: $(g \cdot f)(x)$.

  Solution:

Step 1   The expressions for $f(x)$ and $g(x)$ are given as $f(x) = x + 3$ and $g(x) = x + 2$.

Step 2   Substituting into $(g \cdot f)(x) = g(x) \cdot f(x)$, we get $(g \cdot f)(x) = (x + 2)(x + 3)$.

Step 3   Multiplying out the brackets and simplifying gives $(g \cdot f)(x) = x^2 + 5x + 6$.

Example: If $g(x) = 2x^2 + 3$ and $h(x) = x - 5$, find: $\left(\frac{g}{h}\right)(x)$.

  Solution:

Step 1   We have $g(x) = 2x^2 + 3$ and $h(x) = x - 5$. We must also note that for $h(x)$, we cannot have $x = 5$ because that would cause division by zero.

Step 2   Inserting these into the division expression gives us $\left(\frac{g}{h}\right)(x) = \frac{2x^2 + 3}{x - 5}$.

Step 3   The expression is simplified to $\frac{2x^2 + 3}{x - 5}$, with a note that the function is undefined for $x = 5$.

13.4   Composition of Functions

Composition of functions is a mathematical operation where two functions are combined in such a way that the output of one function becomes the input to the other. This results in a new function that represents the sequence of operations of the composed functions.

Step
By
Step

To compose two functions $f(x)$ and $g(x)$, apply these steps:

Step 1   Identify $g(x)$, the inner function, which will be substituted into $f(x)$, the outer function.

Step 2   Replace the variable x in the outer function $f(x)$ with the expression for $g(x)$.

Example: Let us use $f(x) = 3x+4$ and $g(x) = 7x-1$. Find $(f \circ g)(x)$.

  Solution:

Step 1   Identify the inner function $g(x)$ which is $7x-1$, and the outer function $f(x)$ which is $3x+4$.

Step 2   Substitute $g(x)$ into $f(x)$ to get:

$$f(g(x)) = f(7x-1),$$

which simplifies to $3 \times (7x-1)+4 = 21x-3+4$. Thus, $(f \circ g)(x) = 21x+1$.

Example: Now, let us use $f(x) = 5x-2$ and $g(x) = 7x$. Find $(g \circ f)(4)$.

  Solution:

Step 1   Compute $f(4)$ which gives: $f(4) = 5 \times 4 - 2 = 20 - 2 = 18$.

Step 2   Substitute the value from $f(4)$ into $g(x)$ to find $g(f(4))$: $g(18) = 7 \times 18 = 126$.
  Hence, $(g \circ f)(5) = 126$.

13.5 Practices

  Fill in the Blank:

1) Given $h(x) = -3x+2$. Evaluate $h(\underline{\hspace{2cm}}) = -4$.

2) Equation $f(x) = 7x+4$ represents a function f. Compute $f(2) = \underline{\hspace{2cm}}$.

3) Establish an equation representing the function g if $g(-1) = 4$ and g is a linear function with a slope of 3.

Select One:

4) Given two functions $f(x) = 3x + 2$ and $g(x) = 2x - 5$, what is $(f+g)(x)$?

A) $5x - 3$

B) $5x + 7$

C) $x - 3$

D) $x + 7$

5) If $f(x) = 4x - 2$ and $g(x) = -x + 3$, what is $(f-g)(x)$?

A) $3x - 5$

B) $5x + 1$

C) $5x - 5$

D) $3x + 1$

6) If $m(x) = 2x + 1$ and $r(x) = 2 - x$, what is $(r - m)(x)$?

A) $2x + 1$

B) $-3x + 1$

C) $-3x + 3$

D) $3x + 1$

7) Given two functions $d(x) = 3x - 1$ and $p(x) = x + 2$, what is $(p+d)(2)$?

A) 6

B) 5

C) 9

D) 1

8) Given two functions $l(x) = x + 2$ and $g(x) = 3x - 4$, what is $(g - l)(-1)$?

A) -4

B) -6

C) -8

D) -10

Solve:

9) If $f(x) = 2x^2 - 3$ and $g(x) = x + 1$, find $(f \times g)(x)$.

10) If $f(x) = x^2 + 2x + 1$ and $g(x) = 3x - 2$, find $\left(\frac{f}{g}\right)(x)$.

11) If $f(u) = 2u^3 + 3$ and $g(u) = 2u - 1$, find $(f \times g)(u)$.

12) If $f(y) = 4y^2 + 5y + 1$ and $g(z) = 2z + 3$, find $\left(\frac{f}{g}\right)(1)$.

13) If $f(t) = 3t^2 - t + 2$ and $g(x) = x - 2$, find $(f \times g)(0)$.

Select One:

14) Let us have two functions $f(x) = 3x + 1$ and $g(x) = x^2$. What will be $(f \circ g)(2)$?

A) 13

B) 17

C) 4

D) 19

15) Take $f(x) = 2x + 3$ and $g(x) = x^2$. What will be $(g \circ f)(-2)$?

A) 25

B) 15

C) 1

D) 16

Answer Keys

1) 2

2) 18

3) $g(x) = 3x + 7$

4) A) $5x - 3$

5) C) $5x - 5$

6) B) $-3x + 1$

7) C) 9

8) C) -8

9) $2x^3 + 2x^2 - 3x - 3$

10) $\frac{x^2 + 2x + 1}{3x - 2}$

11) $4u^4 - 2u^3 + 6u - 3$

12) 2

13) -4

14) A) 13

15) C) 1

Answers with Explanation

1) substitute: $h(x) = -3x + 2 = -4$. Hence $-3x = -4 - 2 = -6$. So, $x = 2$.

2) Substituting $x = 2$ into the function gives $f(2) = 7 \times 2 + 4 = 14 + 4 = 18$.

3) Any linear function can be represented in slope-intercept form as $y = mx + b$. Here, $m = 3$. To find b, substitute: $4 = 3 \times -1 + b$. Hence, $b = 7$ and $g(x) = 3x + 7$.

4) To find $(f + g)(x)$, add $f(x)$ and $g(x)$ together: $(3x + 2) + (2x - 5) = 5x - 3$.

5) To find $(f - g)(x)$, subtract $g(x)$ from $f(x)$:

$$(4x - 2) - (-x + 3) = 4x - 2 + x - 3 = 5x - 5.$$

6) Subtract $m(x)$ from $r(x)$ to find $(r - m)(x)$:

$$(2 - x) - (2x + 1) = 2 - x - 2x - 1 = -3x + 1.$$

7) First, find the sum of the functions $(p + d)(x) = (x + 2) + (3x - 1)$. Substitute $x = 2$ into $(p + d)(x)$ to get $(p + d)(2) = (2 + 2) + (3(2) - 1) = 4 + 5 = 9$.

8) First, find the difference of the functions $(g - l)(x) = (3x - 4) - (x + 2)$. Substitute $x = -1$ into $(g - l)(x)$ to get $(g - l)(-1) = (3(-1) - 4) - ((-1) + 2) = -7 - 1 = -8$.

9) Multiply $f(x)$ and $g(x)$ together: $(2x^2 - 3)(x + 1) = 2x^3 + 2x^2 - 3x - 3$.

10) The quotient $\left(\frac{f}{g}\right)(x)$ is obtained by dividing $f(x)$ by $g(x)$, resulting in $\frac{x^2 + 2x + 1}{3x - 2}$.

11) To find $(f \times g)(u)$, multiply $f(u)$ by $g(u)$: $(2u^3 + 3)(2u - 1) = 4u^4 - 2u^3 + 6u - 3$.

12) First, substitute 1 into $f(y)$ and $g(z)$: $f(1) = 4(1)^2 + 5(1) + 1 = 10$ and $g(1) = 2(1) + 3 = 5$. Then, divide $f(1)$ by $g(1)$ to find $\left(\frac{f}{g}\right)(1) = \frac{10}{5} = 2$.

13) First, substitute 0 into $f(t)$ and $g(x)$: $f(0) = 3(0)^2 - 0 + 2 = 2$ and $g(0) = 0 - 2 = -2$. Then, multiply

$f(0)$ by $g(0)$ to find $(f \times g)(0)$: $2 \times -2 = -4$.

14) We first find $g(2)$ which is $2^2 = 4$. Then we put this value into the $f(x)$ function: $f(4) = 3 \times 4 + 1 = 13$. So, $(f \circ g)(2) = f(g(2)) = f(4) = 13$.

15) We first find $f(-2)$ which is $2 \times (-2) + 3 = -1$. Then we put this value into the $g(x)$ function: $g(-1) = (-1)^2 = 1$. So, the answer is 1.

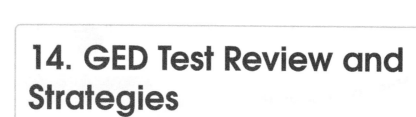

14. GED Test Review and Strategies

14.1   GED Test Review

The General Educational Development Test, often referred to as the GED or high school equivalency diploma, stands as a standardized examination with nationwide recognition in all 50 states across the USA.

At present, the GED is administered in a computer-based format and is accessible at numerous testing centers throughout the country. The GED comprises four subject area assessments:

- **Reasoning through language arts**
- **Mathematical reasoning**
- **Social studies**
- **Science**

Section	Overview	Testing Time	Passing Score
Reasoning Through Language Arts	Reading and Writing Skills	150 minutes	145
Mathematical Reasoning	Quantitative Math and Algebra	115 minutes	145
Science	Life, earth, and space, and physical sciences	90 minutes	145
Social Studies	Geography, civic, economics, and U.S. history	90 minutes	145

The GED *Mathematical Reasoning* test is a crucial component of the GED examination, aimed at assessing your mathematical proficiency. This comprehensive assessment spans a duration of 115 minutes, presented as a single, undivided section. It delves into a wide array of mathematical concepts, encompassing fundamental topics, quantitative problem-solving, and challenging algebraic questions.

There are two parts on the mathematical reasoning section:

- **The first part** comprises 5 questions and is characterized by a notable restriction: the use of calculators is not permitted. It aims to evaluate your core understanding of mathematical principles and problem-solving abilities without relying on external aids.

- **The second part** of the test is a more extensive evaluation, consisting of 41 questions. Here, you can use a calculator. This allowance is designed to facilitate your approach to complex quantitative challenges and algebraic problem-solving.

By understanding the test structure and being well-versed in calculator techniques, you'll enhance your readiness and confidence for the GED Mathematical Reasoning test. For further guidance on utilizing the calculator during your GED Math examination, please refer to: `EffortlessMath.com/blog/ged-calculator`

14.2   GED Math Question Types

The GED Math test includes a range of enhanced question formats:

- **Multiple-Choice:** This is the most common question type where test-takers must choose the correct answer from several options, typically four or five.

- **Multiple-Select:** Unlike multiple-choice, here, test-takers must select all correct answer choices from a list, and there may be more than one correct option.

- **Fill-in-the-Blank:** Test-takers provide their answers by typing them into a designated space, often containing numerical or textual responses.

- **Drag-and-Drop:** In this format, test-takers use a "draggable" tool to move answers to the appropriate location or matching question. Sometimes, multiple target regions are given to choose from.

- **Matching:** Test-takers check boxes when data in one column corresponds to data in a row, similar to True or False questions.

- **Table-Entry:** This question type is used with tables of values that have two columns with a few empty cells. Test-takers input a number into specific cells to fill the table correctly.

14.3   How is the GED Scored?

Each of the GED subject area tests is assessed using a scoring scale ranging from 100 to 200 points. To successfully attain your GED credential, you are required to achieve a minimum score of 145 on each of the four subject tests. This cumulative score ensures that you have earned a total of at least 580 points out of a maximum potential score of 800.

Keep in mind that you must pass each subject test individually. This means you need to score at least 145 in each section of the test. Even if you perform exceptionally well on one subject test and accumulate a total score of 580 or more, it won't count as a passing score if you haven't met the minimum score requirement (145 points) in each of the individual subject tests.

You have four potential score outcomes achievable on the GED Test:

- **Not Passing:** This signifies that your score falls below 145 on any of the four tests. If you do not pass, you have the option to reschedule up to two times a year to retake any or all the subjects of the GED test.

- **Passing Score/High School Equivalency:** This score indicates that your score falls within the range of 145-164. It's important to note that points earned in one subject of the test do not carry over to the other subjects.

- **College Ready:** Achieving a score between 165-175 demonstrates career and college readiness. A College Ready score suggests that you may not require placement testing or remediation before starting a college degree program.

- **College Ready + Credit:** If your score is 175 or higher, it indicates that you've already mastered some skills typically taught in college courses. Depending on a school's policy, this can potentially translate into earning college credits, which can save you time and money during your college education.

14.4   GED Math Test-Taking Strategies

Successfully navigating the GED Math test requires not only a solid understanding of mathematical concepts but also effective problem-solving strategies. In this section, we explore a range of strategies to optimize your performance and outcomes on the GED Math test. From comprehending the question and using informed guessing to finding ballpark answers and employing backsolving and numeric substitution, these strategies will empower you to tackle various types of math problems with confidence and efficiency.

#1 Understand the Questions and Review Answers

Below are a set of effective strategies to optimize your performance and outcomes on the GED Math test.

- **Comprehend the Question:** Begin by carefully reviewing the question to identify keywords and essential information.

- **Mathematical Translation:** Translate the identified keywords into mathematical operations that will enable you to solve the problem effectively.

- **Analyze Answer Choices:** Examine the answer choices provided and identify any distinctions or patterns among them.

- **Visual Aids:** If necessary, consider drawing diagrams or labeling figures to aid in problem-solving.

- **Pattern Recognition:** Look for recurring patterns or relationships within the problem that can guide your solution.

- **Select the Right Method:** Determine the most suitable strategies for answering the question, whether it involves straightforward mathematical calculations, numerical substitution (plugging in numbers), or testing the answer choices (backsolving); see below for a comprehensive explanation of these methods.

- **Verification:** Before finalizing your answer, double-check your work to ensure accuracy and completeness.

Let's review some of the important strategies in detail.

#2 Use Educated Guessing

This strategy is particularly useful for tackling problems that you have some understanding of but cannot solve through straightforward mathematics. In such situations, aim to eliminate as many answer choices as possible before making a selection. When faced with a problem that seems entirely unfamiliar, there's no need to spend excessive time attempting to eliminate answer choices. Instead, opt for a random choice before proceeding to the next question.

As you can see, employing direct solutions is the most effective approach. Carefully read the question, apply the math concepts you've learned, and align your answer with one of the available choices. Feeling stuck? Make your best-educated guess and move forward.

Never leave questions unanswered! Even if a problem appears insurmountable, make an effort to provide a response. If necessary, make an educated guess. Remember, you won't lose points for an incorrect answer, but you may earn points for a correct one!

#3 Ballpark Estimates

A *"ballpark estimate"* is a *rough approximation*. When dealing with complex calculations and numbers, it's easy to make errors. Sometimes, a small decimal shift can turn a correct answer into an incorrect one, no matter how many steps you've taken to arrive at it. This is where ballparking can be incredibly useful.

If you have an idea of what the correct answer might be, even if it's just a rough estimate, you can often eliminate a few answer choices. While answer choices typically account for common student errors and closely related values, you can still rule out choices that are significantly off the mark. When facing a multiple-choice question, deliberately look for answers that don't even come close to the ballpark. This strategy effectively helps eliminate incorrect choices during problem-solving.

#4 Backsolving

A significant portion of questions on the GED Math test are presented in multiple-choice format. Many test-takers find multiple-choice questions preferable since the correct answer is among the choices provided. Typically, you'll have four options to choose from, and your task is to determine the correct one. One effective approach for this is known as *"backsolving."*

As mentioned previously, solving questions directly is the most optimal method. Begin by thoroughly examining the problem, calculating a solution, and then matching the answer with one of the available choices. However, if you find yourself unable to calculate a solution, the next best approach involves employing *"backsolving."*

When employing backsolving, compare one of the answer choices to the problem at hand and determine which choice aligns most closely. Frequently, answer choices are arranged in either ascending or descending order. In such cases, consider testing options B or C first. If neither is correct, you can proceed either up or down from there.

#5 Plugging In Numbers

Using numeric substitution or *'plugging in numbers'* is a valuable strategy applicable to a wide array of math problems encountered on the GED Math test. This approach is particularly helpful in simplifying complex questions, making them more manageable and comprehensible. By employing this strategy thoughtfully, you can arrive at the solution with ease.

The concept is relatively straightforward. Simply replace unknown variables in a problem with specific values. When selecting a number for substitution, consider the following guidelines:

- Opt for a basic number (though not overly basic). It's generally advisable to avoid choosing 1 (or even 0). A reasonable choice often includes selecting the number 2.

- Avoid picking a number already present in the problem statement.

- Ensure that the chosen numbers are distinct when substituting at least two of them.

- Frequently, the use of numeric substitution helps you eliminate some of the answer choices, so it's essential not to hastily select the first option that appears to be correct.

- When faced with multiple seemingly correct answers, you may need to opt for a different set of values and reevaluate the choices that haven't been ruled out yet.

- If your problem includes fractions, a valid solution might require consideration of either *the least common denominator (LCD)* or a multiple of the LCD.

- When tackling problems related to percentages, it's advisable to select the number 100 for numeric substitution.

It is Time to Test Yourself

Take a GED Math practice test to recreate the test day scenario. Once you've completed it, evaluate your performance by using the provided answer key.

- **Gather your supplies:** Ensure you have a pencil and a calculator ready before starting the test.

- **Question types:** There are two types of questions you'll encounter:

  1) Multiple choice questions where have four or more answer choices for these questions.

  2) Grid-ins questions: You'll need to write your answer in the provided box.

- **Don't be afraid to guess:** It's perfectly fine to make educated guesses. Remember, there are no penalties for wrong answers.

- **Formula sheet:** You'll have access to a formula sheet during the test. This sheet contains important formulas related to geometry and algebra. You don't need to memorize them; focus on how to apply them effectively.

- **Review your work:** After completing the test, take some time to go over the answer key. It will help you identify where you made mistakes and areas that need improvement.

- **Stay calm and confident:** Believe in yourself and your abilities. You've got this!

15. Practice Test 1

GED Mathematics Formula Sheet (You can take to the test)

Area of a:

Parallelogram	$A = bh$
Trapezoid	$A = \frac{1}{2}h(b_1 + b_2)$

Surface Area and Volume of a:

Rectangular/Right Prism	$SA = ph + 2B$	$V = Bh$
Cylinder	$SA = 2\pi rh + 2\pi r^2$	$V = \pi r^2 h$
Pyramid	$SA = \frac{1}{2}ps + B$	$V = \frac{1}{3}Bh$
Cone	$SA = \pi r + \pi r^2$	$V = \frac{1}{3}\pi r^2 h$
Sphere	$SA = 4\pi r^2$	$V = \frac{4}{3}\pi r^3$

(p = perimeter of base B; $\pi \approx 3.14$)

Algebra

Slope of a line	$m = \frac{y_2 - y_1}{x_2 - x_1}$
Slope-intercept form of the equation of a line	$y = mx + b$
Point-slope form of the Equation of a line	$y - y_1 = m(x - x_1)$
Standard form of a Quadratic equation	$y = ax^2 + bx + c$
Quadratic formula	$x = \frac{-b \pm \sqrt{b^2 - 4ac}}{2a}$
Pythagorean theorem	$a^2 + b^2 = c^2$
Simple interest	$I = prt$

(I = interest, p = principal, r = rate, t = time)

15.1   GED Mathematical Reasoning Practice Test

Part 1 (Non-Calculator)

5 Questions

Total time for two parts (Non-Calculator, and Calculator parts): 115 Minutes

You may NOT use a calculator on this part.

1) A rectangular poster has a width of 6 cm and a height of 8 cm. What is the length of the diagonal of the poster?

☐ A. 10 cm

☐ B. 12 cm

☐ C. 14 cm

☐ D. 16 cm

2) Which of the following values for x and y satisfy the following system of equations?

$$\begin{cases} x + 2y = 5 \\ 3x - y = 4 \end{cases}$$

☐ A. $x = \frac{7}{13}, y = \frac{11}{13}$

☐ B. $x = \frac{13}{7}, y = \frac{11}{7}$

☐ C. $x = \frac{11}{7}, y = \frac{7}{22}$

☐ D. $x = 4, y = 0.5$

3) Evaluate the expression:

$$8 - 2 \times (3 + 7) + \frac{18}{3 - 1} - 4.$$

Write your answer in the box. ☐

4) A skateboarder starts moving from a point and accelerates at a constant rate. The equation $v = 3t + 4$ describes this situation, where v is the velocity in meters per second and t is the time elapsed in seconds. Which statement best describes the skateboarder's velocity, based on this equation?

☐ A. Starting from a velocity of 4 meters per second, the skateboarder is accelerating at a rate of 3 meters per second per second.

☐ B. Starting from a velocity of 4 meters per second, the skateboarder is decelerating at a rate of 3 meters per second per second.

☐ C. Starting from a velocity of 3 meters per second, the skateboarder is accelerating at a rate of 4 meters per second per second.

☐ D. Starting from a velocity of 3 meters per second, the skateboarder is decelerating at a rate of 4 meters per second per second.

5) A cyclist is participating in a race. The total distance of the race is 120 kilometers and the cyclist maintains an average speed of 30 kilometers per hour throughout the race. Estimate the time it will take for the cyclist to finish the race.

☐ A. 3 hours

☐ B. 4 hours

☐ C. 5 hours

☐ D. 6 hours

Part 2 (Calculator)

41 Questions

Total time for two parts (Non-Calculator, and Calculator parts): 115 Minutes

You can use a calculator on this part.

6) A cone has a height of 9 cm and a radius of 7 cm. What is the volume of the cone in cubic centimeters? ($\pi = 3.14$).

☐ A. 462 cm³

☐ B. 1386 cm³

☐ C. 862 cm³

☐ D. 1226 cm³

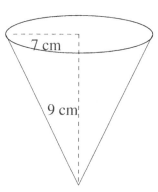

7) Emily is considering investing $3500 in two different savings programs offered by her bank:

- Savings Plan X offers a 4.2% annual interest rate, compounded annually.

- Savings Plan Y provides a simple annual interest rate of 3.8%.

If Emily decides to invest her money for 5 years, which of the following statements will be true at the end of the investment period?

☐ A. Plan X would provide Emily with approximately $65 more interest than Plan Y.

☐ B. Plan Y would provide Emily with approximately $65 more interest than Plan X.

☐ C. Plan X would provide Emily with approximately $134 more interest than Plan Y.

☐ D. Plan Y would provide Emily with approximately $134 more interest than Plan X.

8) The amount of electricity used by a certain machine varies directly with the number of hours it is running. If the machine uses 360 kilowatt-hours of electricity in 15 hours, what is the cost of the electricity used when the machine runs for 8 hours?

☐ A. 96 kilowatt-hours

☐ B. 192 kilowatt-hours

☐ C. 288 kilowatt-hours

☐ D. 384 kilowatt-hours

9) The original price of a refrigerator was $1200. Due to a seasonal sale, its price was reduced to $1020. By what percentage was the price of the refrigerator decreased?

☐ A. 10

☐ B. 12

☐ C. 15

☐ D. 18

10) Consider the linear function that goes through points $(2,3)$ and $(5,7)$. Determine the x-intercept of this linear function's graph.

☐ A. -0.25

☐ B. 0.25

☐ C. -0.75

☐ D. 0.75

11) A rectangular park has a perimeter of 120 meters. If the width of the park is half of its length, what is the length of the park? Write your answer in the box:

12) A researcher discovers a cylindrical fossil with a height of 20 inches and a diameter of 10 inches. Which equation can be used to find V, the volume of the fossil in cubic inches?

☐ A. $V = \pi(10)^2 \times \frac{20}{2}$

☐ B. $V = \pi(5)^2 \times 20$

☐ C. $V = \pi(10) \times 20$

☐ D. $V = \pi(5) \times 20$

13) Which measurements could represent the side lengths in meters of a right triangle?

☐ A. 7 m, 24 m, 25 m

☐ B. 10 m, 10 m, 10 m

☐ C. 6 m, 6 m, 12 m

☐ D. 8 m, 15 m, 16 m

14) Adam's job is to transport goods using his van. He receives a fixed salary each month, plus an additional amount for each mile he travels. In August, Adam traveled 750 miles and received a total of $3750.00. In September, Adam traveled 1100 miles and received a total of $4450.00. Which function can be used to find y, the total amount he is paid in a month if he drives x miles?

   ☐ A. $y = 3.14x$

   ☐ B. $y = 2x + 2250$

   ☐ C. $y = 3.50x + 1500$

   ☐ D. $y = 192x + 3.14$

15) Angles C and D are complementary angles. The measure of angle C is $40°$. The measure of angle D is $(5y + 7)°$. Which equation can be used to find the value of y?

   ☐ A. $40° + (5y + 7)° = 90°$

   ☐ B. $40° = (5y + 7)°$

   ☐ C. $40° + (5y + 7)° = 180°$

   ☐ D. $40° + (5y + 7)° = 360°$

16) The average height of 12 female athletes in a team is 165 cm, and the average height of 18 male athletes in the same team is 175 cm. What is the average height of all 30 athletes on the team? Write your answer in the box:

17) Consider parallelogram ABCD where angle $ABC = (3x + 10)°$ and angle $BCD = (2x - 5)°$. Find the value of x. Write your answer in the box:

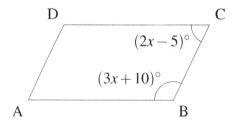

18) A car travels a distance of 120 kilometers in 3 hours. Which function has a slope that best represents the speed (rate) of the car?

   ☐ A. $y = 40x$

   ☐ B. $y = 30x$

   ☐ C. $y = 0.5x$

   ☐ D. $y = x + 120$

19) In a box of chocolates, $\frac{2}{3}$ are milk chocolate and the rest are dark chocolate. If Julia eats $\frac{1}{2}$ of the milk chocolates and all of the dark chocolates, what fraction of the original box of chocolates is left?

☐ A. $\frac{1}{6}$

☐ B. $\frac{1}{3}$

☐ C. $\frac{1}{2}$

☐ D. $\frac{2}{3}$

20) A map is drawn to scale with 1 inch representing 25 miles. If a certain road is 150 miles long, how long is it on the map, in inches?

☐ A. 6 inches

☐ B. 7 inches

☐ C. 8 inches

☐ D. 10 inches

21) A large decorative planter in a park is shaped like an inverted cone with a base diameter of 4 feet and a height of 3 feet. What is the volume of the planter in cubic feet?

☐ A. 4π cubic feet

☐ B. 8π cubic feet

☐ C. 12π cubic feet

☐ D. 16π cubic feet

22) Which set of ordered pairs represents a function with a unique value of y for each x?

☐ A. $\{(3,7), (6,4), (3,2), (5,1)\}$

☐ B. $\{(-1,3), (1,3), (-1,2), (2,3)\}$

☐ C. $\{(7,2), (8,3), (9,5), (10,7)\}$

☐ D. $\{(6,9), (6,-9), (7,11), (8,13)\}$

23) The schoolyard includes a section that is half a square and half a semicircle. If the square has a side length of 10 meters and the diameter of the semicircle is also 10 meters, what is the total area of the section in square meters?

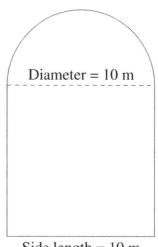

☐ A. $75\pi + 100$ square meters

☐ B. $25\pi + 100$ square meters

☐ C. $12.5\pi + 100$ square meters

☐ D. $50 + 100$ square meters

24) A student is considering various loan options for a 5000 dollars student loan. Which loan option results in the least total interest paid?

    ☐ A. A 3-year loan with a 4.5% annual simple interest rate

    ☐ B. A 4-year loan with a 3.5% annual simple interest rate

    ☐ C. A 5-year loan with a 3% annual simple interest rate

    ☐ D. A 2-year loan with a 5% annual simple interest rate

25) The chart below shows the decline in the population of a rare species over a 10-year period. Which equation best models the relationship between x, the number of years, and y, the remaining population in thousands?

☐ A. $y = -15x + 150$

☐ B. $y = -10x + 200$

☐ C. $y = -20x + 250$

☐ D. $y = -25x + 300$

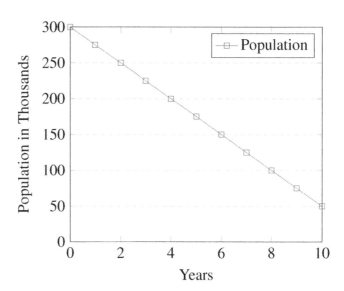

26) If the average of four numbers 14, 17, 23, and x is 19, what is the value of x? Write your answer in the box.

27) A shipping container in the shape of a rectangular prism has a base that measures 4 feet by 5 feet. If the total surface area of the container is 94 square feet, what is the height of the container in feet?

☐ A. 2 ft

☐ B. 3 ft

☐ C. 4 ft

☐ D. 5 ft

28) What value of x makes the following equation true?

$$\frac{32}{4} = \frac{80}{x+2}.$$

☐ A. 6

☐ B. 8

☐ C. 10

☐ D. 12

29) On the coordinate plane, two points $(1, -3)$ and $(3, 1)$ lie on a line. Determine the slope and y-intercept of this line.

☐ A. Slope = 2, y-intercept = −4

☐ B. Slope = 2, y-intercept = −5

☐ C. Slope = −2, y-intercept = 5

☐ D. Slope = −2, y-intercept = −2

30) Consider the following screen sizes given by their diagonal measurements in inches. Which screen size has the largest diagonal measurement?

☐ A. W

☐ B. X

☐ C. Y

☐ D. Z

screen	size
W	$\sqrt{50}$
X	$\sqrt{18}$
Y	$4\sqrt{2}$
Z	$3\sqrt{3}$

31) Express 8500000 as a number in scientific notation.

☐ A. 8.5×10^5

☐ B. 8.5×10^6

☐ C. 8.5×10^7

☐ D. 8.5×10^8

32) Identify the coordinate pair that satisfies the equation $2x + 3y = 6$.

☐ A. $(6, -2)$

☐ B. $(1, 1)$

☐ C. $(2, 0)$

☐ D. $(3, -2)$

33) Solve for x in the equation $2^3 + 5^2 + x - 6 = 23$.

☐ A. $x = 0$

☐ B. $x = -2$

☐ C. $x = -4$

☐ D. $x = 6$

34) For the quadratic function $f(x) = 2x^2 - 4x - 1$, determine which statement is incorrect.

☐ A. The axis of symmetry of the function f is $x = 1$.

☐ B. The zeros of f are real numbers.

☐ C. The vertex form of f includes a negative coefficient for the squared term.

☐ D. The graph of f opens upwards.

35) Calculate the height of a triangle with an area of 54 square units and a base of 6 units.

☐ A. 18 units

☐ B. 9 units

☐ C. 12 units

☐ D. 15 units

36) A plant is being watered daily, and the volume of water in its pot is increasing steadily. Initially, the pot has 40 liters of water. Every day, 2 liters of water are added to the pot. Which function represents v, the volume of water in the pot after n days?

☐ A. $v = 2n + 40$

☐ B. $v = 2n - 40$

☐ C. $v = 40n + 2$

☐ D. $v = -40n + 2$

37) If 60% of a class are boys, and 20% of boys play basketball, what percent of the class plays basketball?

☐ A. 8%

☐ B. 12%

☐ C. 15%

☐ D. 20%

38) Eight measurements of rainfall in a region have an average of 22 *mm*. If a ninth measurement, which is greater than 40 *mm*, is added to the data, what are the possible new averages? (Choose one or more suitable options)

☐ A. 23 *mm*

☐ B. 24 *mm*

☐ C. 25 *mm*

☐ D. 26 *mm*

☐ E. 27 *mm*

39) Consider a trapezoid in which the lengths of the two parallel sides are 10 *cm* and 6 *cm*, and the non-parallel sides are both 8 *cm*. If the height of the trapezoid is 5 *cm*, what is its area? Write your answer in the box.

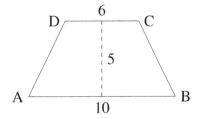

40) A factory quality control team inspects a batch of 5000 lightbulbs. In a sample of 200 lightbulbs, they find that 10 lightbulbs are defective. How many lightbulbs in the entire batch should the quality control team expect to be defective?

☐ A. 200

☐ B. 225

☐ C. 250

☐ D. 275

41) How many positive integers are solutions to the inequality $2x - 3 < 15$?

☐ A. 7

☐ B. 8

☐ C. 9

☐ D. 10

42) Analyze the model of boxes below to find the value of x.

☐ A. $x = \frac{1}{6}$

☐ B. $x = \frac{2}{6}$

☐ C. $x = \frac{3}{6}$

☐ D. $x = \frac{2}{3}$

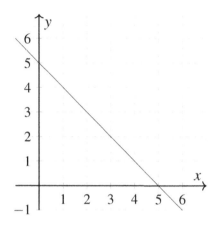

43) Consider the graph below. What is the equation of the line?

☐ A. $y = x + 5$

☐ B. $y = -x + 5$

☐ C. $y = x - 5$

☐ D. $y = -x - 5$

44) A container holds only red pens and blue pens. The ratio of the number of red pens to blue pens is 5:6. Which of the following could be the total number of pens in the container? (Pick one or more appropriate options)

☐ A. 330

☐ B. 550

☐ C. 660

☐ D. 780

☐ E. 945

45) What value on the number line corresponds to the square root of 30?

☐ A. A

☐ B. B

☐ C. C

☐ D. D

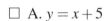

46) Which square pyramid would have a volume equal to 120 cubic units?

☐ A. A pyramid with a base side length of 6 units and height of 3 units

☐ B. A pyramid with a base side length of 9 units and height of 6 units

☐ C. A pyramid with a base side length of 18 units and height of 2 units

☐ D. A pyramid with a base side length of 6 units and height of 10 units

Answer Keys

1) A. 10 cm

2) B. $x = \frac{13}{7}, y = \frac{11}{7}$

3) -7

4) A.

5) B. 4 hours

6) A. 462 cm^3

7) C.

8) B. 192 kilowatt-hours

9) C. 15

10) A. -0.25

11) 40 meters

12) B. $V = \pi(5)^2 \times 20$

13) A. 7 m, 24 m, 25 m

14) B. $y = 2x + 2250$

15) A. $40° + (5y + 7)° = 90°$

16) 171 cm

17) 35

18) A. $y = 40x$

19) B. $\frac{1}{3}$

20) A. 6 inches

21) A. 4π cubic feet

22) C. $\{(7,2), (8,3), (9,5), (10,7)\}$

23) C. $12.5\pi + 100$ square meters

24) D.

25) D. $y = -25x + 300$

26) The value of x is 22.

27) B. 3 ft

28) B. 8

29) B. Slope = 2, y-intercept = -5

30) A. W

31) B. 8.5×10^6

32) A. $(6, -2)$

33) C. $x = -4$

34) C.

35) A. 18 units

36) A. $v = 2n + 40$

37) B. 12%

38) Options C, D, and E are correct.

39) 40 cm^2

40) C. 250

41) B. 8

42) D. $x = \frac{2}{3}$

43) B. $y = -x + 5$

44) Options A, B, and C: 330, 550, and 660

45) D. D

46) D.

Answers with Explanation

1) The diagonal of the rectangular poster forms a right triangle with the width and height of the poster. To find the length of the diagonal (d), we can use the Pythagorean theorem:

$$d^2 = w^2 + h^2.$$

Here, w and h represent the width and height of the poster, respectively. Given that the width is $6\,cm$ and the height is $8\,cm$, we substitute these values into the equation:

$$d^2 = 6^2 + 8^2 = 36 + 64 = 100 \Rightarrow d = 10 \ cm.$$

Therefore, the length of the diagonal of the poster is $10\,cm$, which corresponds to option A.

2) Using elimination method, we find $x = \frac{13}{7}$ and $y = \frac{11}{7}$. Here we want to eliminate y. We multiply the second equation by 2:

$$\begin{cases} x + 2y = 5 \\ 3x - y = 4 \end{cases} \Rightarrow \begin{cases} x + 2y = 5 \\ 6x - 2y = 8 \end{cases}$$

Now add two equations:

$$(x + 2y) + (6x - 2y) = 5 + 8 \Rightarrow 7x = 13 \Rightarrow x = \frac{13}{7}.$$

Substituting $x = \frac{13}{7}$ in the first equation:

$$\frac{13}{7} + 2y = 5 \Rightarrow 2y = 5 - \frac{13}{7} = \frac{22}{7} \Rightarrow y = \frac{11}{7}.$$

Thus, the solution to the system is $x = \frac{13}{7}$ and $y = \frac{11}{7}$.

3) To solve this problem, follow the order of operations:

$$8 - 2 \times (3+7) + \frac{18}{3-1} - 4 = 8 - 2 \times 10 + \frac{18}{2} - 4 \quad \text{(Inside parentheses)}$$

$$= 8 - 20 + 9 - 4 \quad \text{(Multiplication and division)}$$

$$= -12 + 9 - 4$$

$$= -3 - 4$$

$$= -7.$$

So, the value of the expression is -7.

4) According to the equation $v = 3t + 4$, the velocity v increases by 3 meters per second for every additional second of time t. At $t = 0$, the initial velocity is 4 meters per second. Therefore, the skateboarder starts at 4 meters per second and accelerates at 3 meters per second per second, making option A correct.

5) To estimate the time required for the cyclist to finish the race, you can use the formula:

$$\text{Time} = \frac{\text{Distance}}{\text{Speed}}.$$

Plugging in the given values:

$$\text{Time} = \frac{120 \text{ kilometers}}{30 \text{ kilometers per hour}} = 4 \text{ hours}.$$

So, it will take 4 hours for the cyclist to finish the race, which corresponds to option B.

6) The formula for the volume V of a cone is:

$$V = \frac{1}{3}\pi r^2 h.$$

where r is the radius and h is the height.

Plugging in the given values $r = 7$ cm and $h = 9$ cm:

$$V = \frac{1}{3}\pi (7\,\text{cm})^2 (9\,\text{cm}) = 147\pi \approx 462\,\text{cm}^3.$$

So, the volume of the cone is approximately 462 cubic centimeters, which corresponds to option A.

7)

- Savings Plan X (Compounded Annually):

$$A = P(1+r)^t = \$3500 \times (1+0.042)^5 \approx \$4299.39.$$

- Savings Plan Y (Simple Interest):

$$A = P + Prt = \$3500 + \$3500 \times 0.038 \times 5 = \$4165.$$

The interest earned from Plan X is approximately \$799.39, and from Plan Y is \$665. Therefore, Plan X would provide Emily with approximately \$134 more interest than Plan Y, which matches option C.

8) Since the amount of electricity used varies directly with the number of hours the machine runs, we can use the formula $y = kx$, where y is the amount of electricity used, x is the number of hours, and k is the constant of variation.

Using the information given, when the machine runs for 15 hours, it uses 360 kilowatt-hours. So, $360 = 15k$ which gives us $k = 24$.

Now, we can find the electricity used when the machine runs for 8 hours:

$$y = 24 \times 8 = 192 \text{ kilowatt-hours.}$$

9) The percentage decrease can be found using the formula:

$$\text{Percentage Decrease} = \left(\frac{\text{Original Price} - \text{New Price}}{\text{Original Price}}\right) \times 100\%.$$

Substituting the given values:

$$\text{Percentage Decrease} = \left(\frac{1200 - 1020}{1200}\right) \times 100\% = \left(\frac{180}{1200}\right) \times 100\% = 15\%.$$

So, the price of the refrigerator was decreased by 15%.

10) First, calculate the slope m using the formula $m = \frac{y_2 - y_1}{x_2 - x_1}$. For the points $(2,3)$ and $(5,7)$, it is:

$$m = \frac{7-3}{5-2} = \frac{4}{3}.$$

Next, substitute the slope and one of the points into the equation $y = mx + b$ and solve for b. Using the point $(2,3)$:

$$3 = \frac{4}{3} \cdot 2 + b \Rightarrow b = 3 - \frac{8}{3} = \frac{1}{3}.$$

So the equation of the line passing through $(2,3)$ and $(5,7)$ is $y = \frac{4}{3}x + \frac{1}{3}$. Setting $y = 0$ to find the x-intercept, we get $x = -0.25$. The y-intercept occurs when $x = 0$, which gives $y = \frac{1}{3}$. These intercepts are marked on the graph. The x-intercept of -0.25 corresponds to option A.

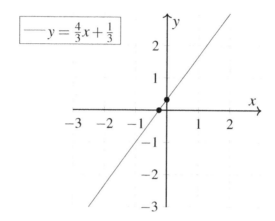

11) Let the length be L meters and the width be W meters. According to the problem, $W = \frac{1}{2}L$. The perimeter P of a rectangle is given by $P = 2L + 2W$. Given $P = 120$ meters, we substitute W to get $120 = 2L + 2(\frac{1}{2}L)$ which simplifies to $120 = 3L$. Therefore, $L = \frac{120}{3} = 40$ meters.

12) The volume V of a cylinder is given by the formula $V = \pi r^2 h$, where r is the radius and h is the height. The diameter of the cylinder is given as 10 inches, so the radius r is half of the diameter, which is $\frac{10}{2} = 5$ inches. Therefore, using the height $h = 20$ inches, the equation for the volume is $V = \pi(5)^2 \times 20$, which corresponds to option B.

13) According to the Pythagorean theorem, for side lengths a, b, and c (where c is the hypotenuse) of a right triangle, the relationship $a^2 + b^2 = c^2$ must hold true.

For option A: $7^2 + 24^2 = 49 + 576 = 625 = 25^2$, which fits the Pythagorean theorem, so it can represent a right triangle.

Options B, C, and D do not satisfy the Pythagorean theorem: For option B: $10^2 + 10^2 = 100 + 100 = 200 \neq 10^2$, and also it represents an equilateral triangle, not a right triangle.

For option C: $6^2 + 6^2 = 36 + 36 = 72 \neq 12^2$.

For option D: $8^2 + 15^2 = 64 + 225 = 289 \neq 16^2$.

Therefore, only option A is correct.

14) To find the function that represents Adam's pay, we can create two equations based on the given data and solve for the fixed salary (f) and the price per mile (m).

- For August: $750m + f = 3750$

- For September: $1100m + f = 4450$

Solving the system of equations, we find that $m = 2$ and $f = 2250$. Therefore, the function that represents Adam's pay is $y = 2x + 2250$, which corresponds to option B.

15) Since angles C and D are complementary, their measures add up to 90 degrees. Given that angle C measures 40 degrees and angle D measures $(5y + 7)$ degrees, we can set up the following equation to find the value of y:

$$40° + (5y + 7)° = 90°.$$

This corresponds to option A.

16) To find the average height, calculate the total height for both female and male athletes and divide by the total number of athletes.

Total height of females $= 12 \times 165 = 1980$ cm.

Total height of males $= 18 \times 175 = 3150$ cm.

Combined total height $= 1980 + 3150 = 5130$ cm.

Average height $= \frac{5130}{30} = 171$ cm.

17) Consecutive angles in a parallelogram are supplementary, which means they add up to $180°$. Thus, we have the equation:

$$(3x + 10) + (2x - 5) = 180°.$$

Simplifying this, we get:

$$5x + 5 = 180° \Rightarrow 5x = 175° \Rightarrow x = 35°.$$

Hence, the value of x is $35°$.

18) The speed of the car can be found by dividing the distance by the time. So, the speed is:

$$\text{Speed} = \frac{\text{Distance}}{\text{Time}} = \frac{120 \text{ km}}{3 \text{ hours}} = 40 \text{ km/hour}.$$

The function that represents this rate of speed as a slope (where y is the distance and x is the time) is $y = 40x$. Thus, option A is correct.

19) The box is divided into milk and dark chocolates. $\frac{2}{3}$ are milk chocolates. If Julia eats $\frac{1}{2}$ of these, she consumes $\frac{1}{2} \times \frac{2}{3} = \frac{2}{6} = \frac{1}{3}$ of the entire box. Since she also eats all of the dark chocolates ($\frac{1}{3}$ of the box), the remaining part is:

$$1 - \left(\frac{1}{3} + \frac{1}{3} \right) = \frac{1}{3}.$$

Therefore, $\frac{1}{3}$ of the original box is left, which is answer B.

20) To find the length on the map, we set up a ratio using the scale. For every 25 miles, there is 1 inch on the map. Therefore, for 150 miles, the road would be:

$$\frac{150 \text{ miles}}{25 \text{ miles/inch}} = 6 \text{ inches.}$$

Hence, the road is 6 inches long on the map, which corresponds to answer A.

21) The formula for the volume of a cone is $\frac{1}{3}\pi r^2 h$. The radius r is half the diameter, so $r = 2$ feet. Plugging in the values, we get:

$$V = \frac{1}{3}\pi(2)^2(3) = \frac{1}{3}\pi \cdot 4 \cdot 3 = 4\pi \text{ cubic feet.}$$

22) A function has a unique y-value for each x-value. Only set C has distinct x-values with corresponding y-values, hence it represents a function.

23) The area of the square is $10 \times 10 = 100$ square meters. The area of the semicircle with a radius of $\frac{10}{2} = 5$ meters is:

$$\frac{1}{2}\pi r^2 = \frac{1}{2}\pi \cdot 5^2 = \frac{25}{2}\pi = 12.5\pi \quad \text{square meters.}$$

Therefore, the total area is $12.5\pi + 100$ square meters.

24) We know that 'Simple Interest = Principal × Rate × Time'. Calculate the total interest for each option:

   A: $5000 \times 0.045 \times 3 = 675$.

   B: $5000 \times 0.035 \times 4 = 700$.

   C: $5000 \times 0.03 \times 5 = 750$.

   D: $5000 \times 0.05 \times 2 = 500$.

The least total interest paid is for option D.

25) The slope of the line representing the population decline can be determined by taking two points from the graph, such as $(0, 300)$ and $(10, 50)$. The slope is $\frac{50-300}{10-0} = -25$. The y-intercept is the initial population, 300. Thus, the equation is $y = -25x + 300$.

26) The average of four numbers is found by adding them together and dividing by 4:

$$\frac{14 + 17 + 23 + x}{4} = 19.$$

Multiply both sides by 4 to clear the denominator:

$$14 + 17 + 23 + x = 76.$$

Combine like terms and subtract 54 from both sides to solve for x:

$$54 + x = 76 \Rightarrow x = 76 - 54 \Rightarrow x = 22.$$

27) Use the surface area formula $S = 2lw + 2lh + 2wh$. For $l = 4$ ft, $w = 5$ ft, and $S = 94$ sq ft, the equation becomes: $40 + 18h = 94$. Solving for h, we get $h = 3$ ft.

28) Consider the proportion:

$$\frac{32}{4} = \frac{80}{x+2}.$$

Cross multiply to solve for x:

$$32(x+2) = 4 \times 80 \Rightarrow 32x + 64 = 320 \Rightarrow 32x = 320 - 64 \Rightarrow 32x = 256 \Rightarrow x = 8.$$

29) The slope m is calculated using the rise over run between the two points:

$$m = \frac{1 - (-3)}{3 - 1} = \frac{4}{2} = 2.$$

To find the y-intercept b, plug the slope and the point $(-3, 1)$ into the equation $y = mx + b$:

$$-3 = 2(1) + b \Rightarrow b = -5.$$

Therefore, the correct answer is B. The following figure represents the graph of the line.

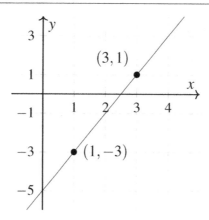

30) Calculate the decimal approximations for each screen diagonal:

$$W \approx 7.07, \quad X \approx 4.24, \quad Y \approx 5.66, \quad Z \approx 5.20.$$

Comparing these values, the largest diagonal measurement is $W = \sqrt{50} \approx 7.07$ inches, making A the correct choice.

31) Moving the decimal 6 places to the left to write the number in scientific notation gives:

$$8500000 = 8.5 \times 10^6.$$

Thus, the correct answer is B.

32) Substituting each coordinate pair into the equation, only $(6, -2)$ satisfies the equation since $2(6) + 3(-2) = 6$. Therefore, the correct answer is A.

33) Simplifying the left side:

$$2^3 + 5^2 + x - 6 = 8 + 25 + x - 6 = 27 + x.$$

Subtract 27 from both sides of the first equation to find x:

$$2^3 + 5^2 + x - 6 = 23 \Rightarrow 27 + x = 23 \Rightarrow x = 23 - 27 \Rightarrow x = -4.$$

Thus, the correct answer is C.

34) The correct vertex form of the function is $f(x) = 2(x-1)^2 - 3$, which has a positive coefficient for the squared term. Therefore, statement C is incorrect.

35) The area A of a triangle is given by $A = \frac{1}{2}bh$ where b is the base and h is the height. Thus:

$$54 = \frac{1}{2} \times 6 \times h \Rightarrow h = \frac{54 \times 2}{6} = 18.$$

The height of the triangle is 18 units, which is answer A.

36) The volume of water starts at 40 liters and increases by 2 liters each day. Thus, the function relating the volume after n days is given by adding $2n$ to the initial volume of 40 liters, which is $v = 2n + 40$, option A.

37) 20% of the 60% boys in the class play basketball, which is $0.20 \times 0.60 = 0.12$ or 12% of the class.

38) The total rainfall of the original eight measurements is $8 \times 22 = 176$ mm. Adding a ninth measurement greater than 40 mm results in a new total greater than 216 ($176 + 40 = 216$ mm). The new average for ninth measurement 40 mm would be $216 \div 9 = 24$ mm. Since the new measurement is higher than 40, the new mean must be more than 24. Therefore, options C and D and E are possible for the ninth measurement greater than 40 mm.

39) To calculate the area of the trapezoid, plug in the lengths of the parallel sides ($b_1 = 10$ cm and $b_2 = 6$ cm) and the height ($h = 5$ cm) into the area formula of trapezoid:

$$\text{Area of trapezoid} = \frac{1}{2}(b_1 + b_2)h = \frac{1}{2}(10 \ cm + 6 \ cm)(5 \ cm) = \frac{1}{2} \times 16 \ cm \times 5 \ cm = 40 \ cm^2.$$

Thus, the area of the trapezoid is 40 cm^2.

40) Using the sample, the defect rate is $\frac{10}{200} = 0.05$ or 5%. Applying this percentage to the entire batch of 5000 lightbulbs gives us:

$$5000 \times 0.05 = 250.$$

So, the team should expect about 250 lightbulbs to be defective.

41) First, we solve the inequality for x:

$$2x - 3 < 15 \Rightarrow 2x < 15 + 3 \Rightarrow 2x < 18 \Rightarrow x < 9.$$

Since x must be a positive integer less than 9, the possible values for x are 1, 2, 3, 4, 5, 6, 7, and 8. Therefore, there are 8 positive integers that satisfy the inequality.

42) There are a total of six boxes marked with x on the left side of the equation and two boxes marked with the number 1 followed by 3 boxes marked with x on the right side. To balance the equation, the two '1' boxes must be equivalent to three x boxes on the left, leaving three x boxes on the left to match the three x boxes on the right. Therefore, $3x$ must be equal to 2. This implies $x = \frac{2}{3}$. Hence, option D is correct.

43) Consider two points $(0,5)$ and $(5,0)$ on the line. Using the formula $m = \frac{y_2 - y_1}{x_2 - x_1}$, the graph of the line has a slope of -1. Also we have $(0,5)$ on the line, so y-intercept is 5. These correspond to the equation $y = -x + 5$.

44) The total number of pens must be divisible by the sum of the parts of the ratio, which is $5 + 6 = 11$. Options A (330), B (550), and C (660) are all multiples of 11, making them possible totals for the pens in the container.

45) The square root of 30 is approximately 5.477. Corresponding to the number line, point D best represents this value.

46) To find the volume of a square pyramid, the formula is $\frac{1}{3}x^2h$, where x is base side length and h is the height. Substituting the given values, $x = 6$ and $h = 10$, the volume is calculated as:

$$V = \frac{1}{3}x^2h = \frac{1}{3} \times 6^2 \times 10,$$

which simplifies to 120 cubic units. Thus, the pyramid with a base side length of 6 units and a height of 10 units has a volume equal to 120.

16. Practice Test 2

GED Mathematics Formula Sheet (You can take to the test)

Area of a:

Parallelogram	$A = bh$
Trapezoid	$A = \frac{1}{2}h(b_1 + b_2)$

Surface Area and Volume of a:

Rectangular/Right Prism	$SA = ph + 2B$	$V = Bh$
Cylinder	$SA = 2\pi rh + 2\pi r^2$	$V = \pi r^2 h$
Pyramid	$SA = \frac{1}{2}ps + B$	$V = \frac{1}{3}Bh$
Cone	$SA = \pi r + \pi r^2$	$V = \frac{1}{3}\pi r^2 h$
Sphere	$SA = 4\pi r^2$	$V = \frac{4}{3}\pi r^3$

(p = perimeter of base B; $\pi \approx 3.14$)

Algebra

Slope of a line	$m = \frac{y_2 - y_1}{x_2 - x_1}$
Slope-intercept form of the equation of a line	$y = mx + b$
Point-slope form of the Equation of a line	$y - y_1 = m(x - x_1)$
Standard form of a Quadratic equation	$y = ax^2 + bx + c$
Quadratic formula	$x = \frac{-b \pm \sqrt{b^2 - 4ac}}{2a}$
Pythagorean theorem	$a^2 + b^2 = c^2$
Simple interest	$I = prt$

(I = interest, p = principal, r = rate, t = time)

16.1   GED Mathematical Reasoning Practice Test

Part 1 (Non-Calculator)

5 Questions

Total time for two parts (Non-Calculator, and Calculator parts): 115 Minutes

You may NOT use a calculator on this part.

1) A classroom is 9 meters long and 7 meters wide. What is the area of the classroom in square meters?

☐ A. 45 m^2

☐ B. 56 m^2

☐ C. 63 m^2

☐ D. 72 m^2

2) In a group of 30 students, 21 students have voted for a class representative. What percentage of the students has not yet voted?

☐ A. 10%

☐ B. 20%

☐ C. 30%

☐ D. 40%

3) If a recipe requires 3.2 liters of milk and milk is sold in 0.8-liter packages, how many packages does one need to buy?

☐ A. 2

☐ B. 3

☐ C. 4

☐ D. 5

4) A small water tank holds 42 liters of water. How much water would 4 such tanks hold together?

☐ A. 168 l

☐ B. 176 l

☐ C. 184 l

☐ D. 196 l

5) A circular garden has an area that is 81π square meters. What is the radius of the garden?

☐ A. 3 m

☐ B. 6 m

☐ C. 9 m

☐ D. 12 m

Part 2 (Calculator)

41 Questions

Total time for two parts (Non-Calculator, and Calculator parts): 115 Minutes

You can use a calculator on this part.

6) Which set of ordered pairs represents y as a function of x?

☐ A. $\{(2,3),(2,-3),(5,7),(5,-7)\}$

☐ B. $\{(3,4),(3,-4),(6,8),(-6,8)\}$

☐ C. $\{(0,0),(1,2),(2,4),(3,6)\}$

☐ D. $\{(7,8),(7,-8),(9,10),(9,-10)\}$

7) What is the slope of the line passing through the points $(2,-1)$ and $(-3,6)$?

☐ A. $\frac{-7}{5}$

☐ B. $\frac{7}{5}$

☐ C. $\frac{-5}{7}$

☐ D. $\frac{5}{7}$

8) A shipping box is in the shape of a rectangular prism with a height of 8 inches, a width of 7 inches, and a length of 14 inches. Determine the total surface area of the box in square inches. Write your answer in the box.

box.

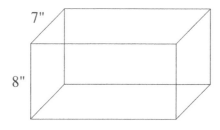

7"

8"

14"

9) Michael invested $500 in two different types of bonds. Bond A provides 4% simple interest per year, and Bond B provides 4% interest compounded annually. What is closest number to the difference in the interest earned by the two bonds after 2 years?

☐ A. $1.00

☐ B. $4.00

☐ C. $16.00

☐ D. $20.00

10) The graph of line N represents $y = \frac{1}{2}x + 2$. If the slope of line N is doubled to create line P, which statement about the graphs of the two lines is true?

☐ A. Line P is perpendicular to line N.

☐ B. Line P is parallel to line N.

☐ C. Line P is steeper than line N.

☐ D. Line P is less steep than line N.

11) The town map is represented on the coordinate grid below with various landmarks. Which landmark on the grid is located at $(-3, -6)$?

☐ A. Library

☐ B. School

☐ C. Cafe

☐ D. Museum

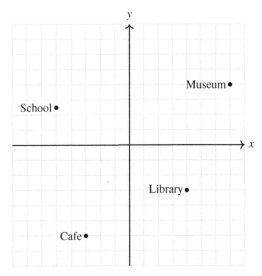

12) A cylindrical tank has a radius of 5 meters and a height of 20 meters. What is the volume of the tank in cubic meters? ($\pi = 3.14$).

☐ A. 1570 m^3

☐ B. 2513.27 m^3

☐ C. 1256.64 m^3

☐ D. 3141.59 m^3

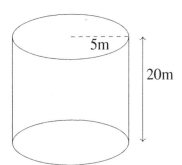

13) What is the value of 9×2.7? Write your answer in the box. ☐

14) Which graph represents the equation $y = 4x - 1$?

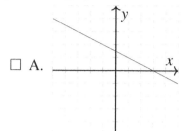 ☐ A.

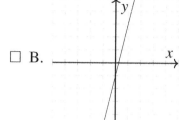 ☐ B.

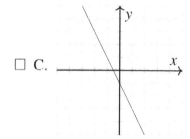 ☐ C.

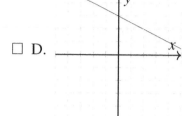 ☐ D.

15) The area of a circle is greater than 100π square inches but less than 200π square inches. Which of the following could be the diameter of the circle? (Choose one or more possible options)

☐ A. 20 *in*

☐ B. 22 *in*

☐ C. 24 *in*

☐ D. 18 *in*

☐ E. 16 *in*

16) Emily needs to have a total score of at least 410 points to qualify for the next round in a competition. If her first four rounds' scores are 85, 90, 88, and 87 points, what is the minimum score she must achieve in the fifth round to qualify? Write your answer in the box. ☐

17) Theater X charges a membership fee of $10.00 and $2.50 per ticket. Theater Y charges a membership fee of $7.00 and $3.00 per ticket. After how many tickets will the total cost at both theaters be equal?

☐ A. 3

☐ B. 6

☐ C. 12

☐ D. 4

18) Two groups of tourists visited a museum on the same day. Group 1 purchased 10 tickets and received a $120 discount. Group 2 purchased 8 tickets and received a $60 discount. If the total cost was the same for both groups, what was the original cost of one ticket?

☐ A. $15

☐ B. $20

☐ C. $30

☐ D. $40

19) Robert lives $8\frac{1}{2}$ miles from his office. He cycles to a train station $\frac{1}{4}$ of the way and then catches a train. How many miles from his home is the train station?

☐ A. $6\frac{3}{4}$

☐ B. $2\frac{1}{8}$

☐ C. $6\frac{1}{2}$

☐ D. $2\frac{1}{4}$

20) Which of the following situations can be represented by the equation $4x + 30 = 8x$?

☐ A. John can fill 4 tanks of water per hour, while Alice can fill 8 tanks per hour. How many hours, x, would it take for John and Alice to fill the same number of tanks?

☐ B. John paid a deposit of $30 for an item. He then pays $8 per day to lay it away. Alice pays $4 per day to lay away the same item. How many days, x, would it take for John and Alice to have paid the same amount?

☐ C. John can write 4 pages per hour, while Alice can write 8 pages per hour. John has already written 30 pages. How many hours, x, would it take for John and Alice to have written the same number of pages?

☐ D. John can earn $8 per hour by washing cars. Alice can earn $30 per day by pet sitting. How many hours, x, would John and Alice need to work for them to have earned the same amount of money?

21) Which of the following graphs represents the compound inequality $2 \leq 3x + 5 < 11$?

☐ A.
```
◄────┼───●───┼───┼───◇──────►
    -2  -1   0   1   2
```

☐ B.
```
◄───┼───┼───┼───●───┼───◇───►
   -2  -1   0   1   2
```

☐ C.
```
◄───┼──●┼───┼───○───┼───┼───►
   -2  -1   0   1   2
```

☐ D.
```
◄───┼───┼──●┼───┼──○┼───►
   -2  -1   0   1   2
```

22) A ramp leads up to a platform as part of an obstacle course. If the height of the platform from the ground is 3 meters and the horizontal distance from the base of the platform to the bottom of the ramp is 4 meters, what is the length of the ramp?

☐ A. 5 meters

☐ B. 6 meters

☐ C. 7 meters

☐ D. 8 meters

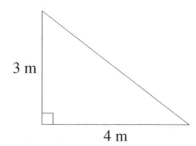

23) At a local art supply store, 5 canvases cost \$30 in total. If each canvas is the same price, what is the cost, c, of each canvas? Write your answer in the box.

24) Which graph best represents the solution set of $y > \frac{1}{2}x - 2$?

☐ A.
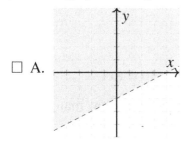

☐ B.
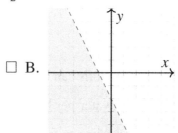

☐ C.
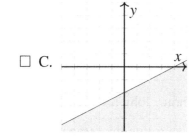

☐ D.

25) The average of seven temperatures recorded at noon throughout a week is 72°F. If an eighth temperature, which is higher than 95°F, is added, which of the following could be the new average temperature? (Select one or more appropriate choices)

☐ A. 72°F

☐ B. 74°F

☐ C. 76°F

☐ D. 78°F

☐ E. 80°F

26) Liam earns a fixed salary plus a commission for each sale he makes.

- In March, Liam made 40 sales and earned a total of \$1200.

- In April, he made 60 sales and earned a total of \$1600.

Which function represents y, Liam's total monthly earnings, based on x, the number of sales he makes?

☐ A. $y = 20x$

☐ B. $y = 30x$

☐ C. $y = 20x + 400$

☐ D. $y = 30x + 200$

27) A study suggests that as the amount of weekly physical activity increases for adults, their reported stress levels decrease. Which scatterplot could support the study's findings?

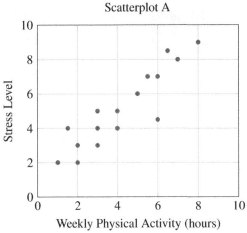

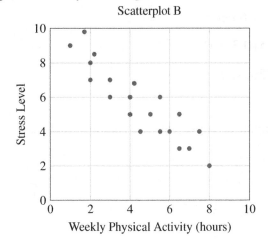

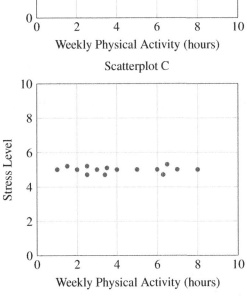

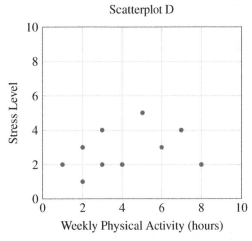

28) Emily's grandparents placed $3000 in a trust fund with a 4.5% annual simple interest rate. There were no further deposits or withdrawals. What would be the amount of interest accrued by the end of 8 years?

☐ A. $1080

☐ B. $1620

☐ C. $108

☐ D. $162

29) If a saline solution contains 20% salt and there are 80 g of salt, what is the total mass of the solution?

☐ A. 350 g

☐ B. 400 g

☐ C. 450 g

☐ D. 500 g

30) Given a sphere with a radius of 10 *cm*, which measurement is closest to the volume of the sphere in cubic centimeters? ($\pi = 3.14$).

    ☐ A. 4186.7 *cm*^{3}

    ☐ B. 8377.6 *cm*^{3}

    ☐ C. 33510.3 *cm*^{3}

    ☐ D. 1256.6 *cm*^{3}

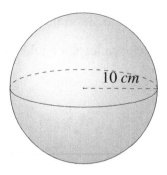

31) What equation represents the function that passes through the points $(0, 2)$ and $(3, -1)$?

    ☐ A. $y = -x + 2$

    ☐ B. $y = \frac{x}{3} + 2$

    ☐ C. $y = -\frac{x}{3} + 2$

    ☐ D. $y = x - 2$

32) A pupil solved the equation $x^2 = 144$ to find the length of the diagonal of a square playground. What is the value of *x*, the length of the diagonal, in meters?

    ☐ A. 11 *m*

    ☐ B. 12 *m*

    ☐ C. 13 *m*

    ☐ D. 14 *m*

33) Determine the value of *x* that satisfies the equation $5x - 2 = 7x + 8$.

    ☐ A. -5

    ☐ B. -10

    ☐ C. 5

    ☐ D. 10

34) Consider the numbers $\sqrt{16}$ and $\frac{20}{7}$. Which of the following values is located between these two numbers?

    ☐ A. $\frac{25}{\pi}$

    ☐ B. $\sqrt{18}$

    ☐ C. 1.1π

    ☐ D. $\frac{\pi}{2}$

35) Determine which graph correctly represents y as a function of x.

☐ A. 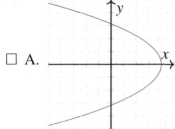   ☐ B.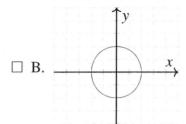

☐ C. 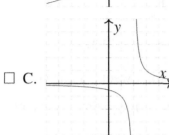   ☐ D.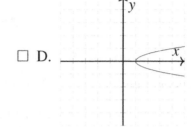

36) Which equation is true when $x = 3$?

    ☐ A. $3x + 5 = 14$

    ☐ B. $5x - 7 = 9$

    ☐ C. $4x + 2 = 13$

    ☐ D. $6x - 9 = 10$

37) Given that the total sum of x boxes must equal the total sum on the right, what is the value of x?

    ☐ A. $x = \frac{1}{6}$

    ☐ B. $x = \frac{2}{3}$

    ☐ C. $x = \frac{3}{6}$

    ☐ D. $x = \frac{4}{3}$

x
x
x
x
x
x

$=$

1
1
1
1
x
x
x

38) A store sells a computer for \$750 before tax. If the local sales tax rate is 6%, what is the total sales tax amount for the computer in dollars and cents? Write your answer in the box. [   ]

39) Jenny is considering a \$2500 loan to repair her car. Which loan option would incur the least amount of interest?

    ☐ A. A 10-month loan with a 6.00% annual simple interest rate

    ☐ B. A 12-month loan with a 5.50% annual simple interest rate

    ☐ C. A 15-month loan with a 5.25% annual simple interest rate

    ☐ D. A 20-month loan with a 5.00% annual simple interest rate

40) The following right triangles are similar. Which proportion can be used to calculate the length of the side *DE*?

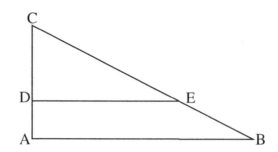

- ☐ A. $\frac{AC}{AB} = \frac{DE}{DC}$
- ☐ B. $\frac{AD}{DC} = \frac{AB}{DE}$
- ☐ C. $\frac{DC}{AC} = \frac{DE}{AB}$
- ☐ D. $\frac{AB}{AD} = \frac{DE}{DC}$

41) Mark has $1000 in his savings account and he deposits $20 each week for *x* weeks. Leah starts with $100 in her savings account and deposits $25 each week for *x* weeks. Which inequality represents the situation when Leah's account balance exceeds Mark's account balance?

- ☐ A. $100 + 25x > 1000 + 20x$
- ☐ B. $20x < 25x + 900$
- ☐ C. $25x < 20x + 1000$
- ☐ D. $1000 + 25x < 100 + 20x$

42) In the figure provided, the radius of the inner circle is 8 *cm* and the diameter of the outer circle is 24 *cm*. Calculate the area of the shaded region.

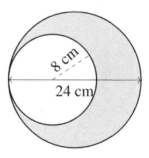

- ☐ A. $32\pi \ cm^2$
- ☐ B. $64\pi \ cm^2$
- ☐ C. $25\pi \ cm^2$
- ☐ D. $80\pi \ cm^2$

43) The area of a circle is less than 49π square centimeters. What could be the possible circumference of the circle? (Select one or more appropriate choices)

- ☐ A. $7\pi \ cm$
- ☐ B. $13\pi \ cm$
- ☐ C. $22\pi \ cm$
- ☐ D. $28\pi \ cm$
- ☐ E. $49\pi \ cm$

44) The area of a rectangle with integer sides is equal to 48 square units. Which of the following could be the perimeter of the rectangle? (Choose one or more suitable options)

- ☐ A. 24 units

☐ B. 26 units

☐ C. 28 units

☐ D. 30 units

☐ E. 32 units

45) Sally's starting salary is $40000 per year and she will receive a salary increase of $3000 per year. Mark's starting salary is $55000 and he will receive a salary increase of $2000 per year. After how many years will Sally's salary be equal to Mark's salary?

☐ A. 5 years

☐ B. 8 years

☐ C. 15 years

☐ D. 20 years

46) A bowl contains different colored marbles numbered from 1 to 20. One marble is selected at random. What is the probability that the marble selected is numbered 11?

☐ A. $\frac{11}{20}$

☐ B. $\frac{9}{20}$

☐ C. $\frac{5}{20}$

☐ D. $\frac{1}{20}$

Answer Keys

1) C. 63 m^2

2) C. 30%

3) C. 4

4) A. 168 l

5) C. 9 m

6) C. $\{(0,0),(1,2),(2,4),(3,6)\}$

7) A. $\frac{-7}{5}$

8) The total surface area of the box is 484 square inches.

9) A. $1.00

10) C. Line P is steeper than line N.

11) C. Cafe

12) A. 1570 m^3

13) 24.3

14) B.

15) B. 22 in and C. 24 in

16) 60 points

17) B. 6

18) C. $30

19) B. $2\frac{1}{8}$

20) C.

21) A.

22) A. 5 meters

23) 6

24) A.

25) C. 76°F, D. 78°F and E. 80°F

26) C. $y = 20x + 400$

27) B.

28) A. $1080

29) B. 400 g

30) A. 4186.7 cm^3

31) A. $y = -x + 2$

32) B. 12 m

33) A. -5

34) C. 1.1π

35) C.

36) A. $3x + 5 = 14$

37) D. $x = \frac{4}{3}$.

38) $45.00

39) A.

40) C. $\frac{DC}{AC} = \frac{DE}{AB}$

41) A. $100 + 25x > 1000 + 20x$

42) D. 80π cm^2.

43) A. 7π cm and B. 13π cm

44) C. 28 units, E. 32 units

45) C. 15 years

46) D. $\frac{1}{20}$

Answers with Explanation

1) The area of a rectangle is found by multiplying the length by the width. Therefore, the area of the classroom is $9\ m \times 7\ m = 63\ m^2$, making option C the correct answer.

2) If 21 students have voted, then $30 - 21 = 9$ students have not voted. The percentage of students not yet voted is $\left(\frac{9}{30}\right) \times 100\%$, which equals 30%, making option C the correct answer.

3) To determine the number of milk packages needed, divide the total amount of milk required by the volume of each package. The recipe requires 3.2 liters, and each package contains 0.8 liters. Therefore, the number of packages needed is:

$$\frac{3.2 \text{ liters}}{0.8 \text{ liters/package}} = \frac{32}{8} = 4 \text{ packages.}$$

Hence, one needs to buy 4 packages of milk.

4) If one tank holds 42 liters, then 4 tanks would hold $42\ l \times 4 = 168\ l$, making option A the correct answer.

5) The area of a circle is given by πr^2, where r is the radius. If the area is 81π, we can set up the equation $\pi r^2 = 81\pi$. Dividing both sides by π, we get $r^2 = 81$. Taking the square root, $r = 9$ meters, which is option C.

6) For a set of ordered pairs to represent a function, each input x must have exactly one output y. Option C is the only set where each x value is paired with only one y value, satisfying the definition of a function.

7) The slope m is calculated by the change in y over the change in x:

$$m = \frac{y_2 - y_1}{x_2 - x_1}.$$

So,

$$m = \frac{6 - (-1)}{-3 - 2} = \frac{7}{-5} = \frac{-7}{5}.$$

8) The surface area A of a rectangular prism is calculated by the formula:

$$A = 2lw + 2lh + 2wh.$$

where l is the length, w is the width, and h is the height of the prism. Substituting the given values:

$$A = 2(14)(7) + 2(14)(8) + 2(7)(8) = 196 + 224 + 112 = 532.$$

Therefore, the total surface area is 532 square inches.

9) For Bond A, (simple interest):

$$P + P \times r \times t = \$500 + \$500 \times 0.04 \times 2 = \$540,$$

so the interest is: $\$540 - \$500 = \$40$.

For Bond B, (compounded interest):

$$P(1 + r)^t = \$500 \times (1 + 0.04)^2 = \$540.80,$$

so the interest is: $\$540.80 - \$500 = \$40.80$.

So, the difference in the interest earned by the two bonds after 2 years is $\$40.80 - \$40 = \$0.8$. The closest option is A.

10) Doubling the slope of line N from $\frac{1}{2}$ to 1 would result in line P with the equation $y = x + 2$. Since the slope of line P is greater than the slope of line N, line P will be steeper than line N, which is option C.

11) On the coordinate grid, the Cafe is the landmark placed at the point $(-3, -6)$.

12) The volume V of a cylinder with radius r and height h is given by $V = \pi r^2 h$. Here, $r = 5\ m$ and $h = 20\ m$, so $V = \pi \times 5^2 \times 20 \approx 1570\ m^3$, which corresponds to option A.

13) First, ignore the decimal and multiply 9 by 27, which is $9 \times 27 = 243$. Since there is one decimal place in 2.7, place the decimal in the result to get 24.3. So, $9 \times 2.7 = 24.3$.

14) The equation $y = 4x - 1$ describes a graph where the slop is positive. The only graph with a positive slope is B.

15) The area of a circle is πr^2, and the diameter is $d = 2r$. The area is between 100π and 200π, so $100\pi < \pi r^2 < 200\pi$. Dividing by π, we get $100 < r^2 < 200$. Taking the square root gives $10 < r < \sqrt{200} \approx 14.14$. Thus, the diameter options that fall within this range are 22 inches and 24 inches.

16) Emily's total score must be at least 410 points after 5 rounds. The sum of her first four rounds is:

$$85 + 90 + 88 + 87 = 350 \text{ points.}$$

Therefore, the minimum score needed in the fifth round is $410 - 350 = 60$ points.

17) Let n be the number of tickets. For the costs to be equal:

$$10 + 2.5n = 7 + 3n.$$

Solving for n, we subtract 7 from both sides to get $3 + 2.5n = 3n$ and then subtract $2.5n$ from both sides to get $3 = 0.5n$. Therefore, $n = 6$.

18) Let p be the original price of one ticket. For Group 1, $10p - 120$ is the total cost, and for Group 2, $8p - 60$ is the total cost. These costs are equal, so:

$$10p - 120 = 8p - 60.$$

Solving for p, we get $2p = 60$, and hence, $p = 30$. Thus, the original cost per ticket is \$30.

19) Robert cycles $\frac{1}{4}$ of the way to the train station. So the distance to the train station is $8\frac{1}{2} \times \frac{1}{4}$. To calculate this, convert the mixed number to an improper fraction: $8\frac{1}{2} = \frac{17}{2}$. Thus, $\frac{17}{2} \times \frac{1}{4} = \frac{17}{8}$, which is $2\frac{1}{8}$ miles.

20) The equation $4x + 30 = 8x$ implies that John has a head start of 30 pages. Since Alice writes more pages per hour, we are trying to find how many hours it will take for Alice to catch up to John's initial lead. The number of pages written by John is 30 plus 4 times the number of hours, while Alice writes 8 pages for each hour they write. This scenario is represented by choice C, as it involves a starting difference (John's 30 pages) and a rate of work that will eventually equalize the total pages written by both John and Alice.

21) To graph the compound inequality $2 \le 3x + 5 < 11$, we first solve for x in both inequalities.

For the left part:

$$2 \leq 3x + 5 \Rightarrow 2 - 5 \leq 3x \Rightarrow -3 \leq 3x \Rightarrow -1 \leq x.$$

For the right part:

$$3x + 5 < 11 \Rightarrow 3x < 11 - 5 \Rightarrow 3x < 6 \Rightarrow x < 2.$$

Combining these, we get $-1 \leq x < 2$. This means that the graph should start at $x = -1$ with a closed circle to include -1 and end at $x = 2$ with an open circle to exclude 2. This corresponds to Option A.

22) To determine the length of the ramp, we apply the Pythagorean theorem in the right triangle formed by the height of the platform, the horizontal distance to the bottom of the ramp, and the ramp itself as the hypotenuse. We have:

$$h^2 = a^2 + b^2 \Rightarrow h^2 = 3^2 + 4^2 \Rightarrow h^2 = 9 + 16 \Rightarrow h = \sqrt{25} \Rightarrow h = 5.$$

Thus, the length of the ramp is 5 meters.

23) Since the total cost for 5 canvases is \$30, the cost of each canvas can be represented by the equation $c = \frac{30}{5}$, which simplifies to $c = 6$.

24) The inequality $y > \frac{1}{2}x - 2$ is graphed by a dashed line with slope $\frac{1}{2}$ and y-intercept at -2, with shading above the line to indicate the area where y is greater than $\frac{1}{2}x - 2$.

25) The sum of the seven temperatures is $7 \times 72 = 504°F$. Adding a temperature that is higher than $95°F$ means the new sum is greater than $504 + 95 = 599°F$. The new average must be greater than $599°F \div 8 = 74.875°F$. The possible new averages from the options that are higher than this value are $76°F$, $78°F$ and $80°F$.

26) To determine the function, we set up two equations based on the given information (s for sales and f for fixed salary):

For March: $1200 = 40s + f$.

For April: $1600 = 60s + f$.

Solving these two equations simultaneously, we find that $s = 20$ and $f = 400$. Therefore, Liam's total earnings based on the number of sales he makes is represented by the function $y = 20x + 400$.

27) Scatterplot B shows a trend where stress levels decrease as weekly physical activity increases, which supports the study's findings. The negative correlation in Scatterplot B, where higher values of weekly physical activity are associated with lower stress levels, aligns with the study's suggestion. Scatterplots A, C, and D do not show this trend and therefore do not support the findings.

28) The interest I earned with simple interest is calculated using the formula $I = P \times r \times t$, where P is the principal amount, r is the annual interest rate (as a decimal), and t is the time in years. So, the interest earned by Emily's trust fund is: $I = \$3000 \times 0.045 \times 8 = \$1080$.

29) If the salt makes up 20% of the solution, then 80 g represents this 20%. To find the total weight of the solution, we set up the equation:

$$80\ g = 0.20 \times \text{total mass}.$$

Solving for the total mass gives us:

$$\text{total mass} = \frac{80\ g}{0.20} = 400\ g.$$

30) The volume V of a sphere is given by the formula $V = \frac{4}{3}\pi r^3$, where r is the radius of the sphere. Plugging in $r = 10\ cm$, the volume is:

$$V = \frac{4}{3}\pi(10)^3 = \frac{4}{3} \times 3.14 \times 1000 = 4186.7\ cm^3.$$

31) To find the equation of the line passing through the points $(0, 2)$ and $(3, -1)$, we can use the slope formula:

$$m = \frac{y_2 - y_1}{x_2 - x_1} = \frac{-1 - 2}{3 - 0} = \frac{-3}{3} = -1.$$

Since the line passes through $(0, 2)$, the y-intercept is 2. Therefore, the equation of the line is $y = -x + 2$.

32) The solution to the equation $x^2 = 144$ is found by taking the square root of both sides. $x = \sqrt{144}$, which simplifies to $x = 12$. Hence, the diagonal of the square playground is 12 meters long.

33) Solving the equation $5x - 2 = 7x + 8$ involves moving the variable terms to one side and the constant terms to the other. Subtracting $5x$ from both sides gives: $-2 = 2x + 8$. Subtracting 8 from both sides gives: $-10 = 2x$, and dividing by 2 gives: $x = -5$.

34) The number $\sqrt{16}$ is 4, and $\frac{20}{7}$ is approximately 2.86. The value of 1.1π (approximately 3.455) is between 2.86 and 4. The value of $\sqrt{18}$ is approximately 4.24, which is greater than $\sqrt{16}$. The value of $\frac{25}{\pi}$ is also greater than 7, and $\frac{\pi}{2}$ is less than both. Therefore, the number that lies between $\sqrt{16}$ and $\frac{20}{7}$ is 1.1π.

35) A function is defined as a relation where each input x has a single output y.

- Option A represents a sideways parabola, which is not a function, because for each x (except $x = 4$) there are two y, but a function is defined by x having only one y.
- Option B represents a circle with a radius of 2, which is not a function because for most values of x, there are two corresponding values of y (one positive and one negative).
- Option C represents a rational function with a vertical asymptote at $x = 2$. This graph will pass the vertical line test because each x value corresponds to exactly one y value.
- Option D represents a sideways parabola, which is not a function because for all x (except $x = 1$) there are two y.

Therefore, the correct graph is given by Option C.

36) Substituting $x = 3$ into the equation $3x + 5$ gives $3(3) + 5 = 9 + 5 = 14$, which is true, making option A correct.

37) There are a total of six boxes marked with x on the left side of the equation and four boxes marked with the number 1 followed by three boxes marked with x on the right side. To balance the equation, the four '1' boxes must be equivalent to three x boxes on the left, leaving three x boxes on the left to match the three x boxes on the right. Therefore, x must be $\frac{4}{3}$ to satisfy the equation. Hence, option D is correct.

38) The sales tax can be found by multiplying the pre-tax price of the computer $750 by the tax rate 6%. Thus, the sales tax is $750 \times 0.06 = \$45.00$.

39) We know that 'Simple Interest = Principal $\times$ Rate $\times$ Time'. Calculate the total interest for each option:

A: $\$2500 \times 0.06 \times \frac{10}{12} = \$125$.

B: $\$2500 \times 0.055 \times 1 = \$137.5$.

C: $\$2500 \times 0.0525 \times \frac{15}{12} \approx \$164$.

D: $\$2500 \times 0.05 \times \frac{20}{12} \approx \$208.3$.

The least total interest paid is for option A which is the least among the options.

40) Since triangles DEC and ABC are similar, their corresponding sides are proportional. In these triangles, DC and AC are corresponding legs, and DE and AB are corresponding legs.

The proportion that relates these corresponding sides is: $\frac{DC}{AC} = \frac{DE}{AB}$. Thus, option C is the correct answer.

41) Mark's savings start at $1000 and increase by $20 each week for x weeks. So, his total savings can be represented as $1000 + 20x$.

Leah's savings start at \$100 and increase by \$25 each week for x weeks. Therefore, her total savings can be represented as $100 + 25x$.

To find when Leah's savings exceed Mark's, we set up the inequality $100 + 25x > 1000 + 20x$. This represents the situation where the total amount in Leah's account is greater than the total amount in Mark's account after x weeks.

Therefore, the correct inequality is Option A: $100 + 25x > 1000 + 20x$.

42) To find the area of the shaded region, we need to subtract the area of the inner circle from the area of the outer circle. The area of the inner circle is:

$$A_{inner} = \pi r_{inner}^2 = \pi(8)^2 = 64\pi \ cm^2.$$

The area of the outer circle is:

$$A_{outer} = \pi r_{outer}^2 = \pi(12)^2 = 144\pi \ cm^2.$$

Therefore, the area of the shaded region is:

$$A_{shaded} = A_{outer} - A_{inner} = 144\pi - 64\pi = 80\pi \ cm^2.$$

43) The area of a circle A is πr^2, and the circumference C is $2\pi r$. If the area is less than 49π, the radius must be less than 7. Therefore, the circumference must be less than $2\pi \times 7 = 14\pi \ cm$. Thus, options A and B are possible circumferences.

44) To have an area less than 48 square units, a rectangle with integer length and width such as 1×48 (perimeter 98), 2×24 (perimeter 52), 3×16 (perimeter 38), 4×12 (perimeter 32), 6×8 (perimeter 28). Therefore, options C and E could be correct perimeters the rectangle.

45) Setting up the equation $40000 + 3000y = 55000 + 2000y$, we solve for y to find the number of years. Subtracting $2000y$ and 40000 from both sides gives us: $1000y = 15000$, so $y = 15$,

46) The formula of probability of event A is:

$$P(A) = \frac{number \ of \ desired \ outcomes}{number \ of \ total \ outcomes}.$$

There is only one marble numbered 11 out of 20, so the probability of selecting it is 1 out of 20, which simplifies to $\frac{1}{20}$.

Author's Final Note

I hope you enjoyed this book as much as I enjoyed writing it. I have tried to make it as easy to understand as possible. I have also tried to make it fun. I hope I have succeeded. If you have any suggestions for improvement, please let me know. I would love to hear from you.

The accuracy of examples and practice is very important to me. We have done our best. But I also expect that I have made some minor errors. Constant improvement is the name of the game. If you find any errors, please let me know. I will fix them in the next edition.

Your learning journey does not end here. I have written a series of books to help you learn math. Make sure you browse through them. I especially recommend workbooks and practice tests to help you prepare for your exams.

I also enjoy reading your reviews. If you have a moment, please leave a review on Amazon. It will help other students find this book.

If you have any questions or comments, please feel free to contact me at drNazari@effortlessmath.com.

And one last thing: Remember to use online resources for additional help. I recommend using the resources on `https://effortlessmath.com`. There are many great videos on YouTube.

Good luck with your studies!

Dr. Abolfazl Nazari

Made in the USA
Middletown, DE
23 August 2024

59634508R00124